20    $12.95 511

SAUNDERS COMPLETE PACKAGE FOR TEACHING ORGANIC CHEMISTRY

Ternay: **Contemporary Organic Chemistry**

Francis: **Student Guide and Solutions Manual to Ternay's Contemporary Organic Chemistry**

Moore and Dalrymple: **Experimental Methods in Organic Chemistry** — *Second Edition*

Pavia, Lampman and Kriz: **Introduction to Organic Laboratory Techniques: A Contemporary Approach**

Banks: **Naming Organic Compounds: A Programmed Introduction to Organic Chemistry** — *Second Edition*

Weeks: **Electron Movement: A Guide for Students of Organic Chemistry**

ELECTRON MOVEMENT:

A Guide for Students of Organic Chemistry

Daniel P. Weeks, Ph. D.

Associate Professor
Seton Hall University
South Orange, New Jersey

 SAUNDERS GOLDEN SUNBURST SERIES

SAUNDERS COLLEGE PUBLISHING · Philadelphia

Saunders College Publishing
West Washington Square
Philadelphia, PA   19105

Library of Congress Cataloging in Publication Data

Weeks, Daniel P

Electron movement.

(Saunders golden series)

1. Chemistry, Physical organic—Programmed instruction.
   I.Title.

QD476.W38   547′.1′22   75–8188

ISBN 0–7216–9143–9

Electronic Movement: A Guide for Students of Organic Chemistry   ISBN 0-7216-9143-9

6789   147   9876

To JOHN and TIM

Two of the best

POSTCARD FROM A STUDENT

Dear Dan,

Last night I was sitting on the shore of San Francisco Bay watching the fog roll in and suddenly I understood what organic chemistry was all about.

Ric

PREFACE

It is often shocking to encounter organic chemistry immediately after a course in general chemistry. Most contemporary general chemistry courses emphasize the physical approach and minimize descriptive chemistry. A thorough dose of this can convince a student that all chemistry is quantitative and theoretical. Then comes organic chemistry and, after the traditional bows to molecular orbital theory, a student finds himself or herself in a new world where equations are seldom balanced, where there is an enormous factual content, and where mathematics is a dirty word.

There are many aspects of organic chemistry that set it apart from the other traditional divisions of chemistry. Among these are the endless variety of structure, the strong dependence on the resonance theory, and the emphasis on mechanisms. The resonance theory and the concept of mechanisms are generalizations which make organic chemistry more understandable. As these techniques are learned, organic chemistry changes from a bewildering array of facts to a unified science in which newly encountered reactions can be understooood from previously learned principles.

When the professor introduces resonance and/or mechanisms he begins using little arrows that resemble fishhooks ($\curvearrowright$). By the use of these arrows, pairs of electrons are moved around molecules with seemingly gay abandon, and appear — as if by wizardry — precisely where the professor needs them. This penchant for moving electron pairs has earned the organic chemist the pejorative "electron pusher" which, like "Yankee Doodle," we wear proudly.

This book uses a programmed approach to accomplish a single purpose. It is designed so that a student may teach herself or himself to push electrons with the same wizardry as the professor. I have observed that students avoid pushing electrons because they do not have ample opportunity to learn how. Thus, they find it difficult to write resonance structures and lose a powerful tool in explaining reactivity. In addition, many students never really become comfortable with the bond making and bond breaking steps of organic mechanisms.

While working through this book, the student will cultivate some very useful skills. First, the construction of Lewis structures of organic compounds and functional groups will be learned. The common functional groups, therefore, will be learned early and in a way that minimizes the necessity of memorization. Second, a systematic method is presented whereby all the possible resonance structures for a molecule or ion can be generated by beginning with one Lewis structure and moving electron pairs. Finally, the processes of bond making and bond breaking, which are commonly encountered in organic reaction mechanisms, are presented. The programmed approach emphasizes repetition and active, rather than passive, participation in the learning process. This should bring students to the point where they are comfortable and confident with the useful skill of electron movement.

This book would not have been written except for a student, Leslie Schweitzer, who was my severest critic and my strongest support. She is the kind of student who requires the professor to do his best. I also thank Professor Andrew Ternay for his perceptive comments, and Mrs. Robert Crisp who typed the manuscript. I am pleased to say that this book was written without the help or encouragement of my colleagues.

Daniel P. Weeks

TO THE PROFESSOR

I have written this program so that a motivated student could get through a substantial part of it *before* he or she begins organic chemistry. Certainly, any student who has had general chemistry will be ready for Chapter 1, Lewis Structures. In Chapters 2 and 3 I have kept organic jargon to a minimum. I have concentrated on teaching the skill of electron pushing and tried to avoid the temptation to teach chemistry, since this is a supplemental text.

I suggest that the students be encouraged to complete Chapter 1 as soon as possible, even before the course begins if that can be arranged. The precise order of assignment for Chapters 2 and 3, which are independent of one another, will depend on the structure of your course. It is not necessary for students to complete Chapter 2 before beginning Chapter 3; each chapter, however, should be done from beginning to end.

The sections on simple ions and benzene and benzenoid aromatic compounds in Chapter 2 should be assigned as soon as resonance is introduced. The sections on more complicated ions and charge separation can be assigned at a time that seems appropriate. Likewise, the first three sections of Chapter 3 should be assigned as soon as mechanisms are introduced, and the final sections when appropriate.

There are certain omissions in this book which should be noted. The program allows a student to learn to generate a series of resonance structures starting with a single structure. However, the matter of which structures will make meaningful contributions to a hybrid and which will not is only briefly noted. Since the ability to distinguish good resonance structures from bad ones requires an intuition that comes only after a longer exposure to organic chemistry, I felt that this subject did not belong in a supplemental text.

No free radicals appear in this text. I confess that this comes from my own predilections toward even–electron chemistry. Once the principles of electron pushing are learned, however, a student will be able to push unpaired electrons as well as paired ones.

The subjects of neighboring group participation, cyclo-additions, and electrocyclic reactions were omitted in an effort to keep the book to a size appropriate for a supplemental text. I believe that students will find these subjects easier as a result of their working through this program.

Finally, students who use this book will be indoctrinated into including all unshared pairs in organic structures. I believe that this habit is enormously helpful in understanding organic reactions and should be encouraged.

TO THE STUDENT

This program takes advantage of two effective devices for learning. First, you will participate actively in the learning process. Because so much of the academic experience consists of receiving information, it should be refreshing to work through a program using your own wits. The second device is repetition. You will see an example of an operation, and then carry out the same operation several times as the supporting material is gradually removed.

Work through a section of the program filling in your answers in pencil. Then check your answers with the tear-out answer sheets covered by an index card. Check your answers carefully for, as in all science, exactness is important. It will be tempting when you are temporarily stuck to go quickly to the answer sheet. However, a short struggle with the program may get you the correct answer to help you teach yourself more effectively. Expect to spend a total of 10 to 14 hours to complete the program. The program has been written in the hope that you will never feel abandoned.

CONTENTS

Chapter 1

LEWIS STRUCTURES 1

    Molecules and Functional Groups 1
    Ions. 22

Chapter 2

RESONANCE STRUCTURES. 39

    Simple Ions. 40
    Benzene and Benzenoid Aromatic Compounds 48
    More Complicated Ions 52
    Molecules Having Resonance Structures
        With Charge Separation 57

Chapter 3

MECHANISMS. 70

    Sigma Bond Breaking 70
    Sigma Bond Making 70
    Simultaneous Bond Making and Breaking 76
    Complex Mechanisms 94
    Rearrangements 100

GLOSSARY OF TERMS 129

LEWIS STRUCTURES

MOLECULES AND FUNCTIONAL GROUPS

SATURATED GROUPS

Proper Lewis structures of organic functional groups can be written by following this brief set of rules.

RULE 1: ▬▬▬▬▬▬▬▬▬▬▬▬▬▬▬▬▬▬▬▬▬▬▬▬▬▬▬▬

Write the molecular skeleton. Historically, the correct skeleton of each functional group had to be deduced from experimental evidence. That has all been done, however, and we shall assume that you know, or will know shortly, that methane's skeleton is

$$
\begin{array}{c}
\mathrm{H} \\
\mathrm{H \quad C \quad H} \qquad \text{and not} \qquad \mathrm{H \quad H \quad C \quad H \quad H} \\
\mathrm{H}
\end{array}
$$

and a carboxylic acid's molecular skeleton is

$$
\begin{array}{c}
\mathrm{O} \\
\mathrm{R \quad C \quad O \quad H} \qquad \text{and not} \qquad \mathrm{R \quad C \quad O \quad O \quad H}
\end{array}
$$

which is often written to save space.

RULE 2: ▬▬▬▬▬▬▬▬▬▬▬▬▬▬▬▬▬▬▬▬▬▬▬▬▬▬▬▬

Assume that all bonds are covalent. This assumption is not always accurate but it works most of the time. As you develop an intuitive sense of organic structure, you will know when to use ionic bonds.

RULE 3: ▰▰▰▰▰▰▰▰▰▰▰▰▰▰▰▰▰▰▰▰▰▰▰▰▰▰

Count the available valence electrons. Each atom in a compound brings into the union a certain number of valence electrons. The number is determined by the atom's group in the periodic table.

1. Hydrogen is a group __I__ element and each hydrogen atom will contribute __1__ valence electron. Carbon is a group _____ (Roman numeral) element and each carbon atom will contribute _____ (number) electrons. Every oxygen atom in a compound will contribute _____ valence electrons.

Chloromethane has the molecular formula CH_3Cl. Its skeleton is

$$\begin{array}{c} H \\ H \quad C \quad Cl \\ \underline{\quad H \quad} \end{array}$$

and the number of valence electrons may be determined as follows. There are three hydrogen atoms each of which contributes __1__ electron, the single carbon atom contributes __4__ electrons, and the single chlorine atom contributes __7__ electrons making a total of __14__. A convenient tabular way to make this calculation is:

$$\begin{array}{ccccc} \underline{3} & H & \underline{1 \times 3} & = & 3 \\ \underline{1} & C & \underline{4 \times 1} & = & 4 \\ \underline{1} & Cl & \underline{7 \times 1} & = & \underline{7} \\ & & & & 14 \end{array}$$

2. Methanol has the molecular formula CH_4O. Its skeleton is

$$\begin{array}{c} H \\ H \quad C \quad O \quad H \\ \underline{\quad H \quad} \end{array} .$$

Each of four hydrogen atoms contributes _____ valence electron, the carbon atom contributes _____, and the oxygen atom contributes _____, making a total of _____.

$$\begin{array}{ccccc} \underline{\quad} & H & \underline{\qquad} & = \\ \underline{\quad} & C & \underline{\qquad} & = \\ \underline{\quad} & O & \underline{\qquad} & = & \underline{\quad} \end{array}$$

RULE 4: ▰▰▰▰▰▰▰▰▰▰▰▰▰▰▰▰▰▰▰▰▰▰▰▰▰▰

Add electrons to the skeleton by making single bonds between the atoms which are bonded and then by providing each atom with a complement of eight electrons (hydrogen requires only two electrons).

3. The skeleton of chloromethane is

_____ .

The central carbon atom is bonded to each of the other atoms by an electron pair (represented by a straight line, —) giving

$$
\begin{array}{c}
\text{H} \\
| \\
\text{H} - \text{C} - \text{Cl} \\
| \\
\text{H}
\end{array}
$$
 _____ .

Now, each hydrogen has two electrons and the carbon atom has eight. However, chlorine must be provided with additional electrons to complete its octet, thus:

$$
\begin{array}{c}
\text{H} \\
| \\
\text{H} - \text{C} - \overline{\underline{\text{Cl}}}| \\
| \\
\text{H}
\end{array}
$$
 _____ .

4. Methanol's skeleton is

_____ .

Connecting all bonded atoms by means of an electron pair (single bond) gives

_____ .

and completing the octet of oxygen gives

_____ .

RULE 5: ███

Count the electrons in the Lewis structure and compare the result with the number derived from Rule 3. If the two numbers are the same the Lewis structure is correct.

5. The structure for chloromethane is

which contains __14__ valence electrons. The number of available valence electrons in chloromethane is ____. The Lewis structure is <u>correct</u>.

6. The structure for methanol is

$$H - \overset{\underset{|}{H}}{\underset{\underset{H}{|}}{C}} - \overline{O} - H$$

which contains ____ valence electrons. The number of available valence electrons is ____. The structure is _____ (correct, incorrect).

Exercises

Using the method outlined above, derive the Lewis structures for the following compounds. The unbonded skeletons are provided.

7. Dimethyl ether (C_2H_6O)

Rule 3

____ H _____ =
____ C _____ =
____ O _____ = ____
                    ═══

Rule 4

H   H
H C O C H
H   H

Rule 5

No. of electrons in structure ____
No. of valence electrons ____
Structure is _____ (correct, incorrect)

8. Methylamine (CH_5N)

Rule 3

____ H _____ =
____ C _____ =
____ N _____ = ____
                    ═══

Rule 4

H   H
H C N
H   H

Rule 5

No. of electrons in structure _____
No. of valence electrons   _____
Structure is _____

9. Methanethiol (CH_4S)

          Rule 3   **Rule 4**

_____ H _____ =   H
_____ C _____ =   H C S H
_____ S _____ = _____
                             =====   H

Rule 5

No. of electrons in structure _____
No. of valence electrons   _____
Structure is _____

10. Methylal ($C_3H_8O_2$)

          Rule 3   **Rule 4**

_____ H _____ =   H   H   H
_____ C _____ =   H C O C O C H
_____ O _____ = _____
                        =====   H   H   H

Rule 5

No. of electrons in structure _____
No. of valence electrons   _____
Structure is _____

UNSATURATED GROUPS

11. Frequently, the application of Rule 5 shows that the number of valence electrons in the trial structure is larger than the number of available valence electrons. The skeleton of ethylene (C_2H_4) is

                      H   H
                          C   C
                      H_____H .

Each of __4__ hydrogen atoms will contribute _____ electron and each of _____ carbon atoms will contribute _____ electrons. The total number of available valence electrons is _____ .

        4   H   1 x 4 =   4
        2   C   4 x 2 =   8
                              12

12. Adding electrons to the skeleton by making single bonds between all bonded atoms gives

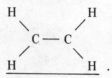

Each hydrogen atom now has a pair of electrons but each carbon has only __6__ electrons. Adding a pair of electrons to each carbon gives

which is the trial structure. The number of electrons in the trial structure is _____. Since this exceeds the number of available valence electrons the structure is <u>incorrect</u>.

RULE 6: ▄▄▄▄▄▄▄▄▄▄▄▄▄▄▄▄▄▄▄▄▄▄▄▄▄▄▄▄

When the number of electrons in the trial structure is larger than the number of available valence electrons, the structure may be corrected by introducing unsaturation.

13. This is done by removing an unshared pair from each of two adjacent atoms and adding one electron pair as a second bond between the atoms. Each such operation removes two electrons from the trial structure. Removing the unshared pairs of electrons on the carbon atoms and adding a second carbon-carbon bond gives

$$
\begin{array}{ccc}
H & & H \\
\diagdown & & \diagup \\
& C = C & \\
\diagup & & \diagdown \\
H & & H
\end{array}\; ,
$$

a structure in which there are four electrons involved in a double bond between the carbon atoms. The trial structure now contains_____ electrons and is correct.

14. Formaldehyde has the skeleton

$$
\begin{array}{ccc}
H & & \\
& C & O \\
H & & \\
\end{array}\;.
$$

Each of _____ hydrogen atoms will contribute _____ electron, the carbon atom, _____ electrons, and the oxygen, _____ electrons. The total number of valence electrons is _____ .

$$
\begin{array}{lll}
\underline{\quad} & H & \underline{\quad\quad} = \\
\underline{\quad} & C & \underline{\quad\quad} = \\
\underline{\quad} & O & \underline{\quad\quad} = \underline{\quad} \\
& & \overline{\overline{\quad\quad}}
\end{array}
$$

Adding single bonds to the skeleton gives

_____

and providing the carbon atom and the oxygen atom with an octet of electrons gives

_____ .

The number of electrons in the trial structure is _____ . The structure is _____ (correct, incorrect). Since the trial structure is incorrect, the pair of unshared electrons on the carbon atom and one of the pairs of unshared electrons on the oxygen atom are removed. Adding a second carbon-oxygen bond gives

_____ .

The trial structure now contains _____ electrons and is _____ (correct, incorrect).

15. The skeleton of acetonitrile is

$$
\begin{array}{cccc}
 & \text{H} & & \\
\text{H} & \text{C} & \text{C} & \text{N} \\
 & \text{H} & &
\end{array}
$$

_____ .

Each of _____ hydrogens will contribute _____ electron, each of _____ carbons will contribute _____ electrons, and the nitrogen will contribute _____ electrons. The total number of valence electrons is _____ .

$$
\begin{array}{lcccl}
\underline{} & \text{H} & \underline{} & = & \\
\underline{} & \text{C} & \underline{} & = & \\
\underline{} & \text{N} & \underline{} & = & \underline{} \\
 & & & & \overline{}
\end{array}
$$

Adding single bonds to the skeleton gives

_____

and providing the carbon and nitrogen atoms with octets gives

_____ .

The number of electrons in the trial structure is _____ . The trial structure is _____ (correct, incorrect). Removing one unshared pair of electrons from carbon and one from nitrogen, and adding a second carbon-nitrogen bond gives

_____ .

The structure now contains _____ electrons and is _____ (correct, incorrect).

Performing the same operation again gives

_____ .

The trial structure now contains _____ electrons and is _____ (correct, incorrect).

Thus, the point is made that removing pairs of unshared electrons from adjacent atoms and adding multiple bonds (adding unsaturation) is continued until the number of electrons in the trial structure is equal to the number of available valence electrons.

*   *   *   *   *

Sometimes, during the operation of adding unsaturation, a decision must be made as to where it is best added.

16. Formic acid has the skeleton

$$
\begin{array}{ccc}
 & & O \\
H & C & \\
 & & O \quad H
\end{array}
$$
 .

The number of available valence electrons is _____ .

$$
\begin{array}{llll}
\underline{\quad} & H & \underline{\qquad} & = \\
\underline{\quad} & C & \underline{\qquad} & = \\
\underline{\quad} & O & \underline{\qquad} & = \quad \underline{\quad} \\
 & & & \underline{\underline{\quad}}
\end{array}
$$

Filling in the skeleton with single bonds gives

$$
\begin{array}{c}
 \qquad\qquad\qquad O \\
 \qquad\qquad\quad \diagup \\
H - C \\
 \qquad\qquad\quad \diagdown \\
 \qquad\qquad\qquad O - H
\end{array}
$$

and adding the appropriate unshared pairs gives

$$
H - \overline{C} \Big\langle {\overset{\displaystyle \overline{O}|}{\underset{\underline{\overline{O}} - H}{}}} \quad .
$$

The number of electrons in the structure is _____ , which is __2__ too many electrons. This structure can be corrected by removing two unshared pairs and making one double bond. However, the double bond could be placed between the carbon atom and either one of the two oxygens. Thus,

$$
H - C \Big\langle {\overset{\displaystyle \overline{O}|}{\underset{\underline{\overline{O}} - H}{}}} \qquad \text{or} \qquad H - C \Big\langle {\overset{\displaystyle \overline{O}|}{\underset{\overline{O} - H}{}}} \quad .
$$

The correct choice is the first structure and is made from the observation that both oxygen atoms in the first structure have the appropriate valence of two. The second structure is less acceptable since it requires that the oxygen atoms have the unfamiliar valences of one and three respectively.[1]

The elements most commonly found in organic compounds are listed below along with their valences.

carbon	4	halogen	1
hydrogen	1	nitrogen	3 (4 in ammonium salts)
	oxygen	2	

One determines the valence of an atom in a structure by counting the number of electron pairs it is <u>sharing</u> with other atoms. The fact that an atom may be sharing more than one pair with another atom (double or triple bond) does not change this. Thus, carbon may exhibit a valence of four in the following ways.

$$
\overset{\displaystyle a}{\underset{\displaystyle c}{b - C - d}} \qquad \overset{\displaystyle b}{a - C = X} \qquad a - C \equiv X
$$

Oxygen may exhibit its valence of two as follows.

$$
a - \overline{O} - b \qquad |\underline{O} = X
$$

---

[1] As we shall see later, the second structure would be less acceptable because it requires a separation of charge as well.

Nitrogen may show a valence of three as follows.

$$a \text{---} \overline{N} \text{---} c \qquad\qquad a \text{---} \overline{N} \text{===} X \qquad\qquad \overline{N} \text{≡} X$$
$$\quad | $$
$$\quad b$$

17. The skeleton of acetyl chloride is

$$\begin{array}{cc} H & O \\ H \quad C & C \\ \underline{\quad H \quad\quad\quad Cl \quad} \end{array}.$$

The number of available valence electrons is _____.

____	H _____	=
____	C _____	=
____	O _____	=
____	Cl _____	= ____

Filling in the skeleton with single bonds gives

_____ .

Adding the appropriate unshared pairs gives

_____ .

The number of electrons in this structure is _____ , which is _____ too many electrons. To correct this structure a pair of unshared electrons could be removed from both the carbon and oxygen and a second bond placed between them giving

_____   (structure I).

Alternatively, a pair of unshared electrons could be removed from both the carbon atom and the chlorine atom and the double bond placed between them resulting in

_____   (structure II).

Structure I requires that oxygen have a valence of _____ , and chlorine, a valence of _____ .
Structure II requires that oxygen have a valence of _____ and chlorine, _____ . Structure _____ (I or II) is correct.

Exercises

Using the method outlined above derive the structures for the following compounds. The unbonded skeletons are provided.

18. Propyne (C_3H_4)

| **Rule 3** | | **Rule 4 (first trial)** |

| _____ H _____ = |
| _____ C _____ = _____ |
| ====== |

Rule 4 (first trial)

```
       H

H   C   C   C   H

       H
_____
```

Rule 5 (first trial)

No. of electrons in structure _____
No. of valence electrons   _____
Structure is _____ (correct, incorrect)

(second trial)   **(third trial)**

_____   _____
_____ _____   _____ _____

   structure is _____   structure is _____

19. Benzene (C_6H_6)

Rule 3   **Rule 4 (first trial)**

_____ H _____ =
_____ C _____ = _____
        ======

```
        H

        C

H   C       C   H

H   C       C   H

        C
_____
        H
```

Rule 5 (first trial)   **(second trial)**

(third trial)   **(fourth trial)**

20. Acetone (C$_3$H$_6$O)

           Rule 3   **Rule 4**

                                          O

                             H   C   H

                            H C   C H

                              H   H

carry on.

21. Formamide (CH$_3$NO)

           Rule 3   **Rule 4**

                                        O

                             H C N H

                                      H

                                _____

carry on.

22. Urea (CH$_4$N$_2$O)

           Rule 3   **Rule 4**

                                        O

                           H N C N H

                                 H   H

carry on.

LARGER MOLECULES

So far, the structures we have written have been of very small molecules. If the procedure outlined were applied scrupulously to writing the Lewis structures of larger molecules the process would become very tedious. However, organic chemistry is fundamentally the chemistry of functional groups. Often in writing mechanisms or other electron-pushing operations it is only necessary to write the Lewis structure of the functional group. The rest of the molecule can be stipulated in one of several shorthand notations that organic chemists are fond of using. Thus,

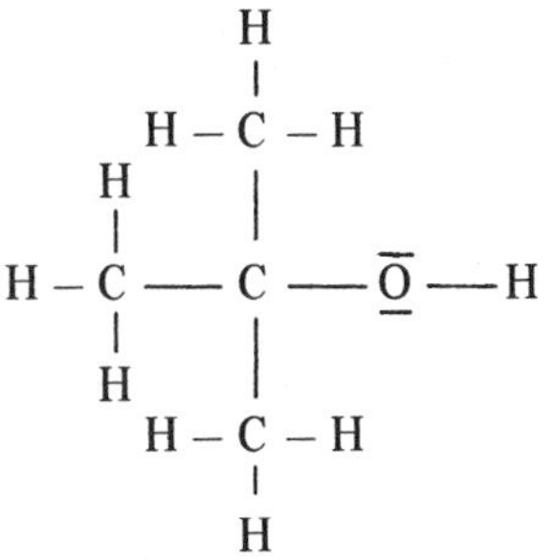

$$
\begin{array}{c}
\text{H} \\
| \\
\text{H}-\text{C}-\text{H} \\
\text{H} \quad | \\
| \\
\text{H}-\text{C}\!-\!-\!\text{C}\!-\!-\!\underline{\overline{\text{O}}}\!-\!\!\text{H} \qquad \text{becomes} \qquad \text{CH}_3\!-\!\underset{\underset{\text{CH}_3}{|}}{\overset{\overset{\text{CH}_3}{|}}{\text{C}}}\!-\!\underline{\overline{\text{O}}}\!-\!\!\text{H} \\
| \\
\text{H} \quad | \\
\text{H}-\text{C}-\text{H} \\
| \\
\text{H}
\end{array}
$$

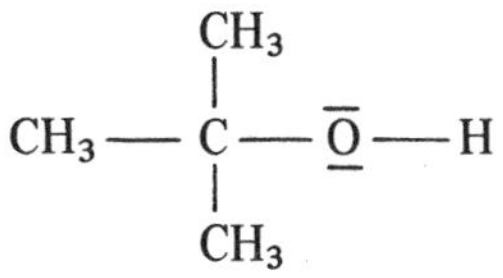

and

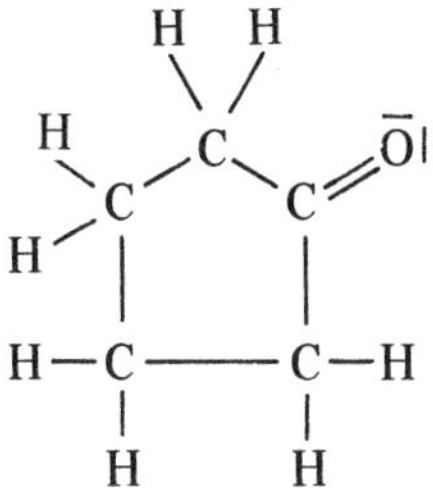

$$
\text{cyclopentane ring with} = \overline{\overline{\text{O}}}| \qquad \text{becomes} \qquad \text{cyclopentanone} = \overline{\overline{\text{O}}}|
$$

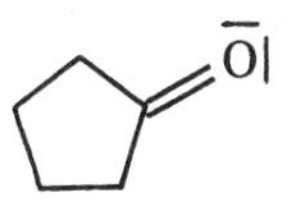

and

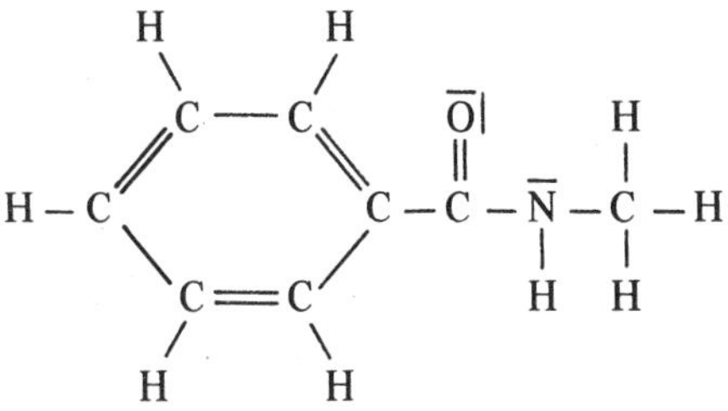

$$
\text{benzene ring}-\overset{\overset{\overline{\overline{\text{O}}}|}{||}}{\text{C}}-\overline{\text{N}}\text{H}-\text{CH}_3 \qquad \text{becomes} \qquad \text{(See Footnote 2.)}
$$

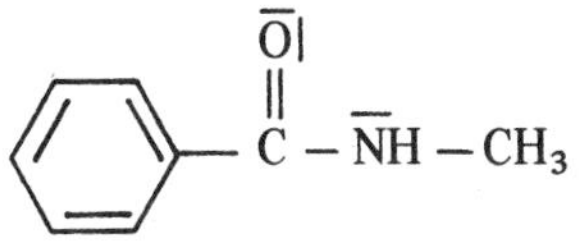

---

[2]Most organic textbooks do not include the unshared pairs in functional groups. The structures above then become

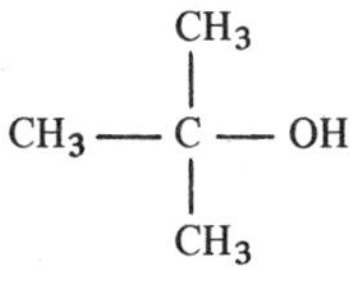

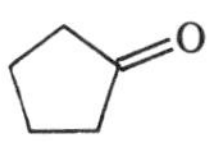

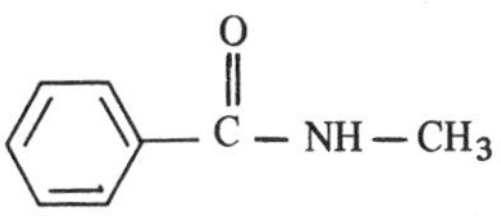

$$
\text{CH}_3\!-\!\underset{\underset{\text{CH}_3}{|}}{\overset{\overset{\text{CH}_3}{|}}{\text{C}}}\!-\!\text{OH} \qquad\qquad \text{cyclopentanone} = \text{O} \qquad\qquad \text{benzene ring}-\overset{\overset{\text{O}}{||}}{\text{C}}-\text{NH}-\text{CH}_3
$$

The idea is to delete the unshared pairs and assume that even the beginning student will understand that they must be there because the octet rule applies. This is really a most unfortunate practice because so much of the chemistry of a functional group is determined by the presence (or absence) of unshared pairs.

In order to write Lewis structures of functional groups attached to any alkyl (R) or aryl (Ar) group, one writes down the skeleton (using some shorthand notation) and then counts the available valence electrons allowing each R or Ar[3] attached directly to the functional group to bring one electron into the union.

23. Phenyl methyl ketone (acetophenone) has the skeleton

The number of available valence electrons is: from the phenyl group, __1__ ; from the methyl group, __1__ ; from the carbon atom, __4__ ; and from the oxygen atom, __6__ . The total number of valence electrons is ____ . Filling in the skeleton with only single bonds gives

---

[3]The use of R or Ar in organic structures seems to confuse some. The letter R is used to denote any alkyl (aliphatic) group and Ar is used to denote any aryl (aromatic) group. This shorthand device allows a chemist to avoid writing down a complicated organic structure when all that needs to be shown is the transformation of a functional group. For example:

$$R - CH_2 - \overline{\underline{O}} - H \xrightarrow{\text{HBr}} R - CH_2 - \overline{\underline{Br}}|$$

is much easier than

$$CH_3 - \underset{\underset{CH_3}{|}}{CH} - CH_2 - \underset{\underset{CH_3}{|}}{CH} - CH_2 - \overline{\underline{O}} - H \xrightarrow{\text{HBr}} CH_3 - \underset{\underset{CH_3}{|}}{CH} - CH_2 - \underset{\underset{CH_3}{|}}{CH} - CH_2 - \overline{\underline{Br}}| \ .$$

In this case R =

$$CH_3 - \underset{\underset{CH_3}{|}}{CH} - CH_2 - \underset{\underset{CH_3}{|}}{CH} -$$

Likewise,

$$Ar - \underset{\overset{\overset{\displaystyle \overline{O}|}{\|}}{}}{C} - \overline{\underline{O}} - H \xrightarrow{\text{SOCl}_2} Ar - \underset{\overset{\overset{\displaystyle \overline{O}|}{\|}}{}}{C} - \overline{\underline{Cl}}|$$

is easier than

In this case Ar =

and adding the appropriate unshared pairs gives

$$\langle\!\!\!\!\!\bigcirc\!\!\!\!\!\rangle - \overline{\underline{C}} - CH_3$$
$$\overset{|\overline{O}|}{\underset{|}{}}$$

The number of valence electrons in this structure is _____ which is _____ too many. Removing an unshared pair from carbon and another from oxygen and placing a second bond between carbon and oxygen gives the correct structure

_____ .

24. The skeleton of benzyldimethylamine is

$$\langle\!\!\!\!\!\bigcirc\!\!\!\!\!\rangle - CH_2 \qquad N \qquad \overset{CH_3}{\underset{CH_3}{}}$$

_____ .

The number of available valence electrons is: from the benzyl group, _____ ; from each of two methyl groups, _____ ; and, from the nitrogen atom, _____ , for a total of _____ . Filling in the skeleton with single bonds gives

_____ .

and adding the appropriate unshared pair gives

_____ .

The number of electrons in the functional group of this structure is _____ and the structure is _____ (correct, incorrect).

25. The skeleton of benzaldoxime is

$$\langle\!\!\!\!\!\bigcirc\!\!\!\!\!\rangle \qquad \overset{H}{\underset{}{C}} \quad N$$
$$O \quad H$$

_____ .

The number of valence electrons is: from the phenyl group, _____ , from each of two hydrogens, _____ ; from the carbon atom, _____ ; from the nitrogen atom, _____ ; and from the oxygen atom, _____ , for a total of _____ . Filling in the skeleton with single bonds and adding the appropriate unshared pairs gives

_____ .

The number of electrons in the functional group of this trial structure is _____ which is _____ too many. Removing an unshared pair from carbon and nitrogen and adding a second bond between them gives

_____ .

in which carbon, nitrogen, and oxygen have their customary valences of _____ , _____ , and _____ respectively. The alternative structure with a double bond between nitrogen and oxygen is

_____ .

This structure is not acceptable because it requires carbon and oxygen to exhibit the unfamiliar valences of _____ and _____ .

Exercises

Derive Lewis structures for the compounds below.

26. 2-phenyl-2-hexanol

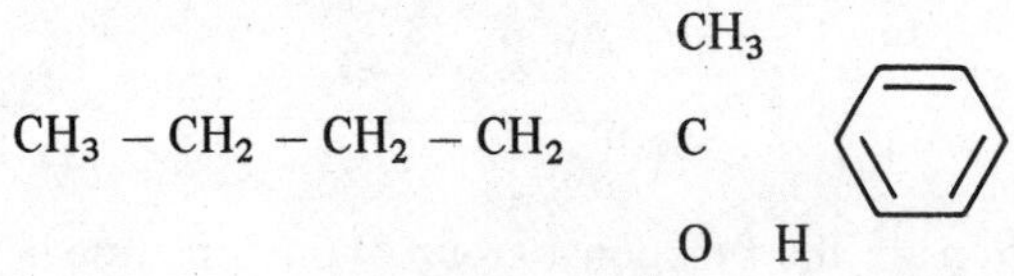

$$CH_3 - CH_2 - CH_2 - CH_2 \quad \overset{CH_3}{\underset{O \; H}{C}} \quad \hexagon$$

27. Furan

H H
C C
H C C H
O

28. Benzophenone phenylhydrazone

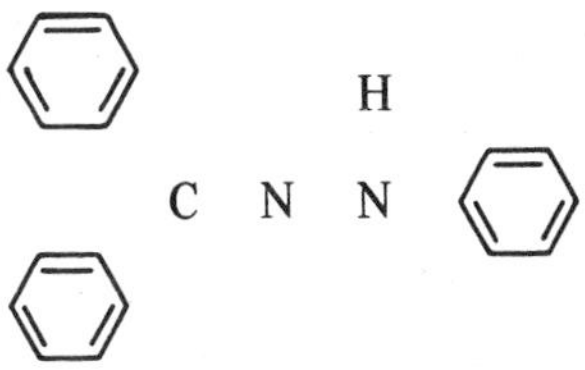

29. Azobenzene

30. Methyl benzimidate

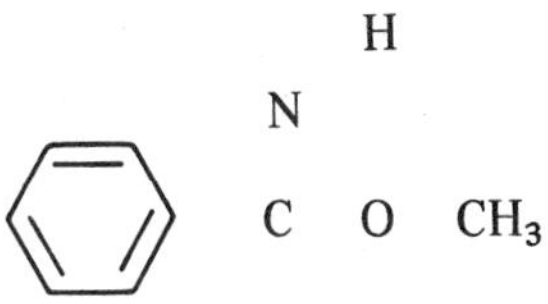

31. Ethyl crotonate (For the purpose of drawing Lewis structures of compounds having more than one functional group, each group can be treated independently.)

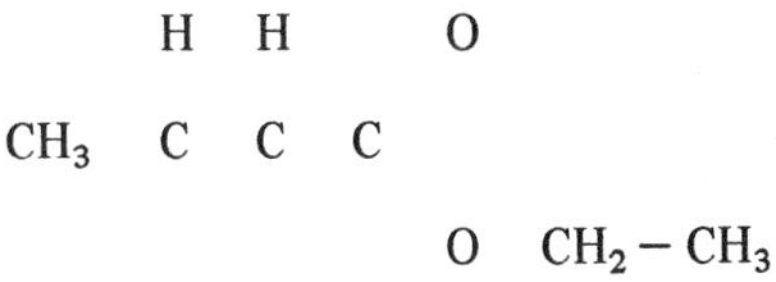

FORMAL CHARGE

Some organic functional groups, although neutral overall, have formal charges on individual atoms. In addition, many of the intermediates which appear in organic reaction mechanisms are charged.

To calculate the formal charge on an atom in a particular structure it is necessary to make a distinction between the electrons which make up an atom's octet and the electrons which formally "belong" to an atom. The distinction is an arbitrary one but it is helpful in calculating formal charge. In any Lewis structure all electrons associated with an atom either as an unshared pair or in bonding to another atom (shared pair) are part of that atom's octet.

Chloromethane has the Lewis structure

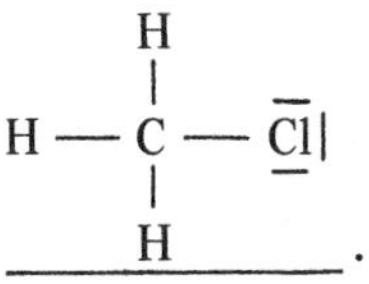

Circling the carbon atom and its octet of electrons gives

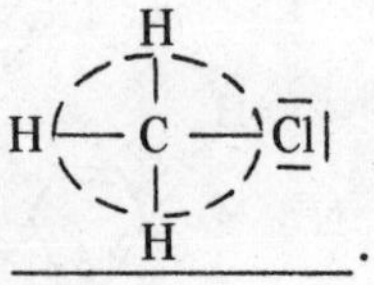

$$
\begin{array}{c}
H \\
| \\
H - C - \overline{Cl}| \\
| \\
H
\end{array}
$$

Circling the chlorine atom and its octet gives

$$
\begin{array}{c}
H \\
| \\
H - C - \overline{Cl}| \\
| \\
H
\end{array}
$$

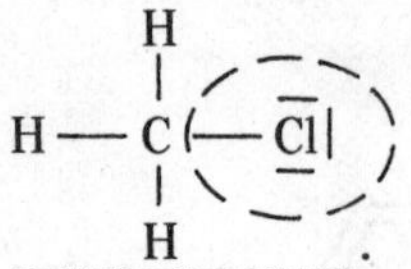

32. The Lewis structure of acetone is

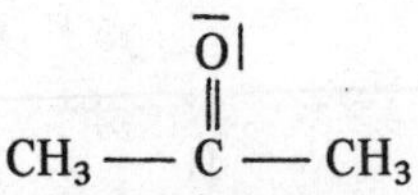

$$
\begin{array}{c}
\overline{O}| \\
\| \\
CH_3 - C - CH_3
\end{array}
$$

Circling the carbonyl carbon, i.e., the carbon atom which is attached to oxygen, and its octet gives

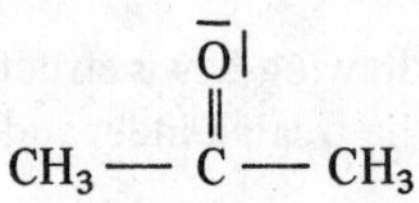

$$
\begin{array}{c}
\overline{O}| \\
\| \\
CH_3 - C - CH_3
\end{array}
$$

Circling the oxygen atom and its octet gives

$$
\begin{array}{c}
\overline{O}| \\
\| \\
CH_3 - C - CH_3
\end{array}
$$

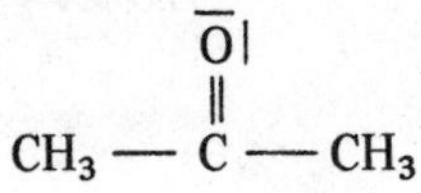

Thus, atoms share electrons in making bonds and a pair of electrons may be included in the octet of two different atoms.

When computing the formal charge on an atom the number of electrons which "belong" to that atom is compared with the number of electrons the atom would have in the unbonded and neutral state. If the two numbers are the same the formal charge on the atom is zero. In a Lewis structure both electrons in an unshared pair belong to the atom and one of every pair of shared (bonding) electrons belongs to the atom.

33. Chloromethane has the Lewis structure

The carbon atom is sharing __4__ electron pairs. In each shared pair the carbon atom "owns" __1__ electron. The number of electrons which "belong" to carbon is _____ . Carbon, being a group _____ element would have __4__ outer shell electrons in the unbonded, neutral state. Therefore, the carbon atom in chloromethane has a formal charge of zero.

34. In the Lewis structure for chloromethane the chlorine atom is sharing _____ electron pair and "owns" _____ of those electrons. Also, the chlorine atom possesses two electrons from each of _____ unshared pairs. The total number of electrons which belong to chlorine is __7__ . Chlorine is a group _____ element. The formal charge on chlorine in chloromethane is _____ .

35. The Lewis structure for acetone is

$$CH_3 - \overset{\overset{\displaystyle \bar{O}|}{\|}}{C} - CH_3 .$$

The carbonyl carbon is sharing _____ pairs of electrons (two carbon-carbon bonds and one carbon-oxygen double bond). From each of those shared pairs the carbonyl carbon "owns" _____ electron. The total number of electrons belonging to the carbonyl carbon is _____. Carbon is a group _____ element. In acetone the formal charge on the carbonyl carbon is _____ .

36. The oxygen atom in acetone possesses _____ unshared pairs and _____ shared pairs of electrons. The number of electrons which belong to oxygen is _____. Oxygen is a group _____ element. The formal charge on oxygen in acetone is_____ .

* * * * *

All of the structures introduced in this Chapter so far have only atoms with formal charge equal to zero. We will now see molecules containing atoms with formal charge other than zero.

37. Nitrobenzene has the skeleton

The number of available valence electrons is: from the phenyl group, _____ ; from the nitrogen atom, _____ ; and from each of two oxygen atoms, _____ , for a total of _____ . Filling in all single bonds and adding the appropriate unshared pairs gives

_____ .

The functional group of this structure contains _____ electrons. Therefore, unshared pairs are removed from the nitrogen atom and one of the oxygen atoms; a double bond is added giving

_____

which has the correct number of electrons. In this structure the nitrogen atom is sharing _____ pairs of electrons. From each shared pair the nitrogen owns _____ electron for a total of _____. Nitrogen is a group _____ element and would have _____ outer shell electrons in the unbonded, neutral state. Since the nitrogen atom in nitrobenzene has one fewer electron than it would in the neutral state it has a formal charge of __+1__.[4] This is added to the Lewis structure as ⊕ giving

38. Nitrobenzene is not an ion. It is a neutral molecule. There must be a formal negative charge somewhere in the molecule to balance the positive charge on the nitrogen. The oxygen atom which is bonded to the nitrogen by a double bond

"owns" _____ unshared pairs of electrons. It is sharing _____ pairs of electrons. The number of electrons owned by the oxygen is _____. Since oxygen is a group _____ element the formal charge on this oxygen atom is _____. The oxygen atom which is bonded to the nitrogen by a single bond

owns _____ unshared pairs of electrons and is sharing _____ pair. The number of electrons owned by this oxygen is _____. This oxygen atom has one more electron than it would have in the neutral state and, thus, has a formal charge of _____. This is added to the Lewis structure as ⊖ giving

which is a complete, correct Lewis structure.[5]

---

[4] Since an electron is negatively charged a shortage of one electron results in a single positive charge (⊕) on an atom. Conversely, an excess of one electron results in a single negative charge (⊖) on an atom. When an atom in a Lewis structure "owns" two less electrons than it would have in the neutral, unbonded state it is denoted by ⊕⊕ or ⊕2 and, conversely ⊖= or ⊖2.

[5] The cogniscenti in the crowd will recognize that this structure is one of two equivalent resonance structures for nitrobenzene. This will come up later in the text.

Exercises

Compute and add on the formal charges in these Lewis structures.

39. Pyridine N-oxide

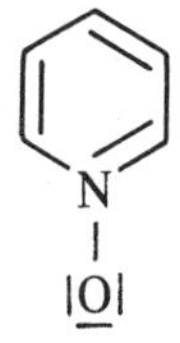

40. Benzenesulfonic acid

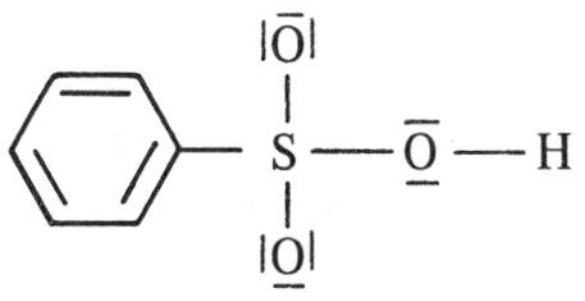

41. N-methyl benzenesulfonamide

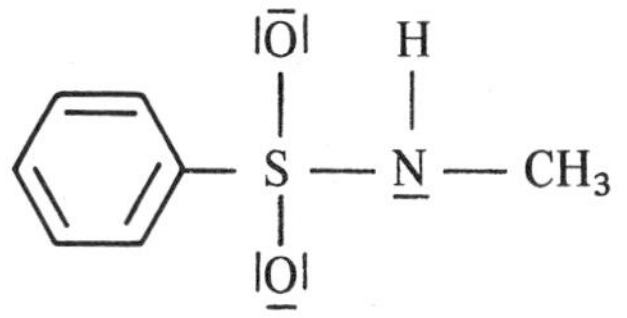

42. Ethylidenetriphenylphosphorane (an ylide)

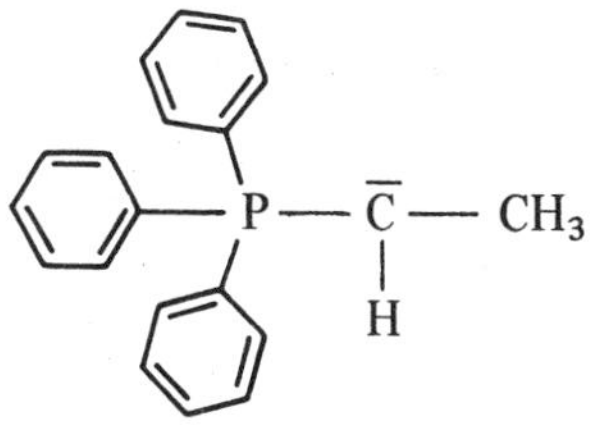

43. Methylazide

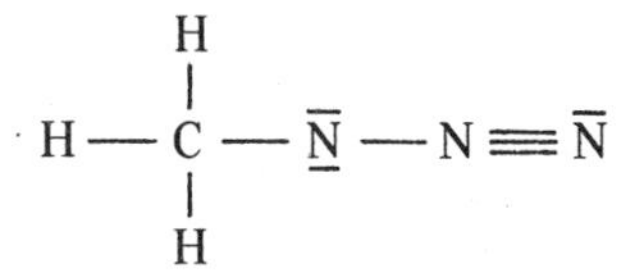

44. Diazomethane

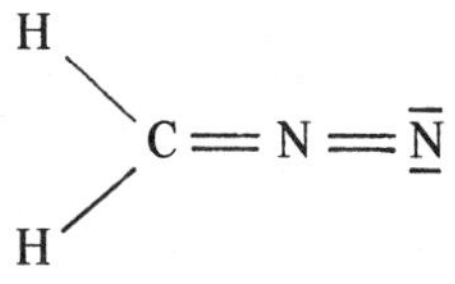

45. Phenylisocyanide

$$\text{⟨benzene ring⟩} - N \equiv \bar{C}$$

46. Phenylcyanide (benzonitrile)

$$\text{⟨benzene ring⟩} - C \equiv \bar{N}$$

47. Trimethylamine oxide

$$CH_3 - \underset{\underset{CH_3}{|}}{\overset{\overset{CH_3}{|}}{N}} - \bar{\underline{O}}|$$

48. Dimethylsulfoxide

$$CH_3 - \underset{\underline{S}}{\overset{|\bar{\underline{O}}|}{|}} - CH_3$$

IONS

The structures encountered so far have been those of molecules, i.e., neutral species. In many cases there was no formal charge anywhere in the structure. In some cases formal charges appeared in the structure but their algebraic sum was zero.

Although the starting materials and products of most organic reactions are molecules, a very large number of organic reactions involve ions as intermediates. Ions are charged species. The algebraic sum of the formal charges in an ion is not zero. With very few exceptions the ions encountered in organic chemistry will have a total charge of +1 or −1. Ions with a total charge of greater than one, which are quite common in inorganic chemistry, are rarely found in organic chemistry.

The ionic intermediates of organic chemistry are usually shortlived species because they are unstable relative to neutral molecules. Nevertheless, the proposed existence of ionic intermediates has contributed enormously to the understanding of organic reactions.

The most direct way to comprehend the structures of ions is to see how they arise in a reaction. This involves some sort of bond breaking or bond making process. Bond breaking and bond making are covered extensively in Chapter III. They will be introduced briefly here.

CATIONS

Consider a molecule consisting of a methyl group attached to chlorine (chloromethane)

$$H - \underset{\underset{H}{|}}{\overset{\overset{H}{|}}{C}} - \bar{\underline{Cl}}|$$

The formal charge on all the atoms in this molecule is zero. Now consider what would result if this molecule were broken at the C–Cl bond so that the two electrons which comprise the C–Cl bond both went with the chlorine.

$$
\begin{array}{ccc}
\quad\; H & & \quad\; H \\
\quad\; | & & \quad\; | \\
H - C - \overline{\underline{Cl}}| & \longrightarrow & H - C \qquad - \overline{\underline{Cl}}| \\
\quad\; | & & \quad\; | \\
\quad\; H & & \quad\; H
\end{array}
$$

49. The usual method is used to calculate the formal charge on these fragments. The carbon atom of the methyl fragment is sharing _____ electron pairs. In each shared pair the carbon "owns" _____ electron. The number of electrons which "belong" to carbon is _____. Carbon, being a group _____ element would have _____ outer shell electrons in the neutral, unbonded state. Since the carbon atom has one fewer electron than it would in the neutral state it has a formal charge of _____. Therefore, the correct Lewis structure for the methyl cation is

$$
\begin{array}{c}
H \\
| \\
H - C^{\oplus} \\
| \\
H
\end{array}
$$

              _____ .

The other fragment is chlorine which now possesses _____ unshared electron pairs. The number of electrons which belong to chlorine is _____. This group VII element has a formal charge of _____.[6]

50. The n-propyl cation can be formed from a molecule such as

$$
\begin{array}{c}
\qquad\qquad\quad H \\
\qquad\qquad\quad | \\
CH_3 - CH_2 - C - \overline{\underline{Cl}}| \\
\qquad\qquad\quad | \\
\qquad\qquad\quad H
\end{array}
$$

    _____ .

When the C–Cl bond is broken so that both electrons go with Cl, the organic fragment formed is

           _____ .

The carbon atom which had been attached to Cl is now sharing _____ electron pairs. In each shared pair the carbon atom owns _____ electron. The number of electrons which belong to

---

[6]This illustrates the very important concept of conservation of charge. In an equation the algebraic sum of the charges on one side must equal the sum on the other side. Thus, in this example, a neutral molecule (charge = 0) yields a cation plus an anion [charge = (+1) + (−1) = 0].

carbon is _____. The formal charge on the carbon atom is _____. The correct Lewis structure for the *n*-propyl cation is

_____.

51. The isopropyl cation can be formed from

$$CH_3 \!-\!\! \underset{\underset{CH_3}{|}}{\overset{\overset{H}{|}}{C}} \!-\! \overline{\underline{Cl}}|$$
_____.

When the C–Cl bond is broken so that both electrons go with Cl (chlorine departs as chloride ion), the organic fragment formed is

_____.

The carbon atom which had been attached to chlorine is now sharing _____ electron pairs. The total number of electrons which belong to carbon is _____. The formal charge on the carbon atom is _____. The correct Lewis structure for the isopropyl cation is

_____.

52. The cyclopentyl cation can be formed from

$$\text{cyclopentane ring with} \begin{array}{c} H \\ \overline{\underline{Cl}}| \end{array}$$.

When the chlorine departs as chloride ion the organic fragment formed is

_____.

The carbon atom which had been attached to chlorine is now sharing _____ electron pairs. The total number of electrons belonging to the carbon atom is _____. The formal charge on the carbon atom is _____. The correct Lewis structure for the cyclopentyl cation is

_____.

53. Methanol, CH_3–$\overline{O}$–H, is a compound in which the formal charge on all the atoms is zero. Consider what results when a proton, H $\oplus$, becomes bonded to methanol by way of one of the unshared electron pairs on the oxygen atom, i.e.,

$$CH_3 — \overline{O} — H$$
$$|$$
$$H$$

In this structure the oxygen atom owns one electron from each of _____ shared pairs and two electrons from _____ unshared pair. The total number of electrons which belong to the oxygen atom is _____. Oxygen is a group _____ element. Since the number of electrons which the oxygen atom owns in this structure is one less than it would have in the neutral, unbonded state, the charge on oxygen is _____. The correct Lewis structure for the conjugate acid of methanol is

_____ .

54. When a proton becomes bonded to diethyl ether, CH_3–CH_2–$\overline{O}$–CH_2–CH_3, by way of one of unshared electron pairs on the oxygen atom, the result is

_____ .

In this structure the oxygen atom owns one electron from each of _____ shared pairs and two electrons from _____ unshared pair. The total number of electrons which belong to oxygen is _____. The formal charge on oxygen is _____. The correct Lewis structure for the conjugate acid of diethyl ether is

_____ .

55. Tetrahydrofuran has the structure,

_____ .

When a proton becomes bonded to tetrahydrofuran the result is

_____ .

In this structure the oxygen atom owns one electron from each of _____ shared pairs and two electrons from _____ unshared pair. The formal charge on the oxygen atom is _____ . The Lewis structure for the conjugate acid of tetrahydrofuran is

_____ .

56. Methylamine,

$$CH_3^3 - \overline{N} - H,$$
$$|$$
$$H$$

has an unshared electron pair on the nitrogen atom. When a proton becomes bonded to methylamine the result is

_____ .

In this structure the nitrogen atom is sharing _____ electron pairs. From each shared pair the nitrogen owns _____ electron for a total of _____ electrons. Nitrogen is a group _____ element. The formal charge on the nitrogen atom is _____ . The Lewis structure for the methyl-ammonium ion is

_____ .

57. When a proton becomes bonded to diethylamine,

$$CH_3 - CH_2 - \overline{N} - CH_2 - CH_3 ,$$
$$|$$
$$H$$

the result is

_____ .

In this structure the nitrogen owns one electron from each of _____ shared pairs. The total number of electrons which belong to nitrogen is _____ . The formal charge on the nitrogen is _____ . The Lewis structure for the diethylammonium ion is

_____ .

58. The structure of pyridine is

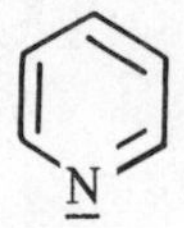

_____ .

When a proton becomes bonded to the nitrogen atom by way of its unshared electron pair the result is

_____ .

In this structure the nitrogen atom is sharing _____ electron pairs. The formal charge on the nitrogen atom is _____ . The Lewis structure for the pyridinium ion is

_____ .

ANIONS

Consider a molecule consisting of a methyl group to which some atom, E, is attached. Assume further that the formal charge on all the atoms in the molecule is zero. Now consider what would result if this molecule were broken at the C–E bond so that the two electrons which comprise the C–E bond both <u>remain</u> with the methyl fragment.

$$
\begin{array}{c}
\quad\;\; H \\
\quad\;\; | \\
H \!-\! C \!-\! E \\
\quad\;\; | \\
\quad\;\; H
\end{array}
\quad \longrightarrow \quad
\begin{array}{c}
\quad\;\; H \\
\quad\;\; | \\
H \!-\! C \!-\! \\
\quad\;\; | \\
\quad\;\; H
\end{array}
\quad E
$$

59. The carbon atom of the methyl fragment owns one electron from each of _____ shared pairs and two electrons from _____ unshared pair. The number of electrons which belong to carbon is _____ . Carbon is a group _____ element. Since the carbon atom has one more electron than it would in the neutral, unbonded state it has a formal charge of $\underline{\;-1\;}$. The Lewis structure for the methyl anion is

$$
\begin{array}{c}
\quad\;\; H \\
\quad\;\; | \quad \ominus \\
H \!-\! C \!-\! \\
\quad\;\; | \\
\quad\;\; H
\end{array}
$$

_____ .

The other fragment must have a formal charge of _____ .

60. The *n*-butyl anion can be formed from a molecule such as

$$
\begin{array}{c}
\qquad\qquad\qquad\; H \\
\qquad\qquad\qquad\; | \\
CH_3 - CH_2 - CH_2 - C - E \;\;.\\
\qquad\qquad\qquad\; | \\
\qquad\qquad\qquad\; H
\end{array}
$$

When the C–E bond is broken so that both electrons remain with the carbon atom, the fragment formed is

_____.

The carbon atom which had been attached to E now owns one electron from each of _____ shared pairs and two electrons from _____ unshared pair. The number of electrons which belong to carbon is _____. The formal charge on the carbon atom is _____. The Lewis structure for the *n*-butyl anion is

_____.

61. The isobutyl anion can be formed from

$$CH_3 - CH - \underset{\underset{CH_3}{|}}{\overset{\overset{H}{|}}{C}} - E \underset{\underset{H}{|}}{}$$

_____.

When the C–E bond is broken so that both electrons remain with the carbon atom, the fragment formed is

_____.

The carbon atom which had been attached to E now owns one electron from each of _____ shared pairs and two electrons from _____ unshared pair. The number of electrons which belong to carbon is _____. The Lewis structure for the isobutyl anion is

_____.

62. When the C–E bond in

$$\bigcirc - \underset{\underset{H}{|}}{\overset{\overset{H}{|}}{C}} - E$$

is broken so that both electrons remain with the carbon atom the fragment formed is

_____ .

The carbon atom which had been attached to E now owns one electron from each of _____ shared pairs and two electrons from _____ unshared pair. The formal charge on the carbon atom is _____ . The Lewis structure for the cyclohexylmethyl anion is

_____ .

63. Ethanol, $CH_3-CH_2-\overline{O}-H$, is a compound in which the formal charge on all the atoms is zero. Under certain conditions the O–H bond can be broken so that both electrons remain with the oxygen atom. The resulting fragment is

$$CH_3 - CH_2 - \overline{\underline{O}}| \; .$$

In this structure the oxygen owns one electron from _____ shared pair and two electrons from each of _____ unshared pairs. The total number of electrons belonging to oxygen is _____ . Oxygen is a group _____ element. The formal charge on the oxygen atom is _____ . The correct Lewis structure for the ethoxide ion is

_____ .

Note that the other fragment, the proton, leaves with a formal charge of +1.

64. The loss of a proton attached to the oxygen atom of *t*-butyl alcohol,

$$CH_3 - \underset{\underset{CH_3}{|}}{\overset{\overset{CH_3}{|}}{C}} - \overline{\underline{O}} - H$$

results in the fragment

_____ .

In this structure the oxygen atom owns one electron from _____ shared pair and two electrons from each of _____ unshared pairs. The number of electrons belonging to oxygen is _____. The formal charge on the oxygen is _____. The Lewis structure for the *t*-butoxide ion is

_____ .

65. A very strong base can remove a proton from methylamine,

$$CH_3 - \overline{N} - H \quad .$$
$$| $$
$$H$$

The proton removed is one of those attached to the nitrogen atom. The resulting fragment is

_____ .

The nitrogen atom now owns one electron from each of _____ shared pairs and two electrons from each of _____ unshared pairs. The number of electrons which belong to the nitrogen atom is _____. Nitrogen is a group _____ element. The formal charge on nitrogen is _____. The Lewis structure for the methylamide ion is

_____ .

66. The loss of a proton from cyclohexylamine,

results in the fragment

_____ .

The number of electrons which belong to the nitrogen atom is _____. The formal charge on the nitrogen atom is _____. The correct Lewis structure for the cyclohexylamide ion is

_____ .

======== ANSWERS ========

CHAPTER I

1. IV, 4, 6

2. 1, 4, 6, 14

    4 H   1 × 4 = 4
    1 C   4 × 1 = 4
    1 O   6 × 1 = 6
                  ——
                  14

3.
```
        H

    H   C   Cl

        H
```

4.
```
        H              H
                       |
    H   C   O   H ,  H—C—O—H ,
                       |
        H              H
```

```
        H
        |
    H — C — O — H
        |
        H
```

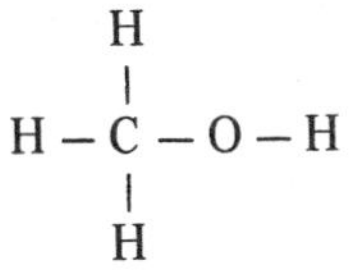

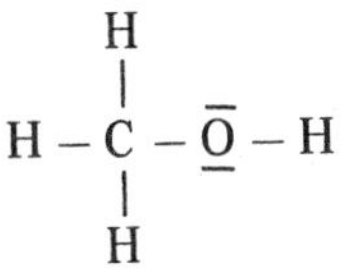

5. 14

6. 14, 14, correct

7. 6 H   1 × 6 = 6
    2 C   4 × 2 = 8
    1 O   6 × 1 = 6
                  ——
                  20

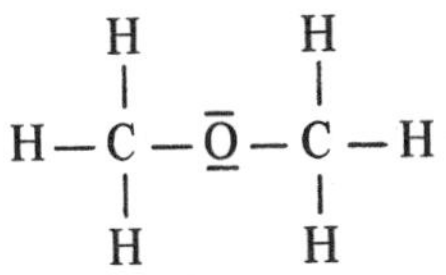

```
        H       H
        |       |
    H — C — O — C — H  , 20, 20, correct
        |       |
        H       H
```

8. 5 H   1 × 5 = 5   ,   H   , 14, 14, correct
    1 C   4 × 1 = 4 | H
    1 N   5 × 1 = 5   H — C — N
                  —— | H
                  14   H

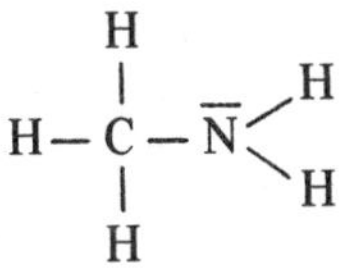

9. 4 H 1 × 4 = 4   ,   , 14, 14, correct
    1 C 4 × 1 = 4
    1 S 6 × 1 = $\underline{6}$
                   $\overline{14}$

$$H-\overset{\displaystyle H}{\underset{\displaystyle H}{C}}-\overline{\underline{S}}-H$$

10. 8 H 1 × 8 = 8   ,   , 32, 32, correct
    3 C 4 × 3 = 12
    2 O 6 × 2 = $\underline{12}$
                   $\overline{32}$

$$H-\overset{\displaystyle H}{\underset{\displaystyle H}{C}}-\overline{\underline{O}}-\overset{\displaystyle H}{\underset{\displaystyle H}{C}}-\overline{\underline{O}}-\overset{\displaystyle H}{\underset{\displaystyle H}{C}}-H$$

11. 1, 4, 12

12. 14

13. 12

14. 2, 1, 4, 6, 12,   2 H 1 × 2 = 2   , $\overset{\displaystyle H}{\underset{\displaystyle H}{>}}C-O,$ $\overset{\displaystyle H}{\underset{\displaystyle H}{>}}\overline{C}-\overline{\underline{O}}|,$
                        1 C 4 × 1 = 4
                        1 O 6 × 1 = $\underline{6}$
                                       $\overline{12}$

    14, incorrect, $\overset{\displaystyle H}{\underset{\displaystyle H}{>}}C=\overline{\underline{O}}|,$ 12, correct

15. 3, 1, 2, 4, 5, 16,   3 H 1 × 3 = 3   ,
                          2 C 4 × 2 = 8
                          1 N 5 × 1 = $\underline{5}$ $H-\overset{\displaystyle H}{\underset{\displaystyle H}{C}}-C-N,$
                                         $\overline{16}$

$H-\overset{\displaystyle H}{\underset{\displaystyle H}{C}}-\overline{\underline{C}}-\overline{\underline{N}}|$, 20, incorrect, $H-\overset{\displaystyle H}{\underset{\displaystyle H}{C}}-\underline{C}=\underline{N}|$, 18, incorrect,

$H-\overset{\displaystyle H}{\underset{\displaystyle H}{C}}-C\equiv N|$, 16, correct

16. 18,   2 H 1 × 2 = 2   , 20
          1 C 4 × 1 = 4
          2 O 6 × 2 = $\underline{12}$
                         $\overline{18}$

17. 24,   3 H 1 × 3 = 3   ,   ,   ,
          2 C 4 × 2 = 8
          1 O 6 × 1 = 6
          1 Cl 7 × 1 = $\underline{7}$
                         $\overline{24}$

$$H-\overset{\displaystyle H}{\underset{\displaystyle H}{C}}-C\overset{\displaystyle O}{\underset{\displaystyle Cl}{<}}$$

$$H-\overset{\displaystyle H}{\underset{\displaystyle H}{C}}-\overline{C}\overset{\displaystyle \overline{\underline{O}}|}{\underset{\displaystyle \overline{\underline{Cl}}|}{<}}$$

26, 2,

$$H-\underset{\underset{H}{|}}{\overset{\overset{H}{|}}{C}}-C\overset{\displaystyle \overline{O}|}{\underset{\displaystyle \overline{Cl}|}{\diagup}}$$
,
$$H-\underset{\underset{H}{|}}{\overset{\overset{H}{|}}{C}}-C\overset{\displaystyle \overline{\overline{O}}|}{\underset{\displaystyle \overline{Cl}|}{\diagdown}}$$
, 2, 1, 1, 2, I

18. 4 H   1 × 4 = 4
     3 C   4 × 3 = $\underline{12}$
                    16
,
$$H-\underset{\underset{H}{|}}{\overset{\overset{H}{|}}{C}}-\underline{C}-\underline{C}-H$$
, 20
  16
  incorrect
,

$$H-\underset{\underset{H}{|}}{\overset{\overset{H}{|}}{C}}-\underline{C}=\underline{C}-H$$
, 18
  16
  incorrect
,
$$H-\underset{\underset{H}{|}}{\overset{\overset{H}{|}}{C}}-C\equiv C-H$$
, 16
  16
  correct

19. 6 H   1 × 6 = 6
     6 C   4 × 6 = $\underline{24}$
                    30
,
(benzene ring structure with alternating bonds)
, 36
  30
  incorrect

(benzene ring structure)
, 34
  30
  incorrect
,
(benzene ring structure)
, 32
  30
  incorrect

(benzene ring structure with two double bonds)
, 30
  30
  correct

20. 6 H   1 × 6 = 6
     3 C   4 × 3 = 12
     1 O   6 × 1 = $\underline{6}$
                    24
,
$$H-\underset{\underset{H}{|}}{\overset{\overset{H}{|}}{C}}-\underset{\underset{H}{|}}{\overset{\overset{|\overline{O}|}{|}}{\underline{C}}}-\overset{\overset{H}{|}}{\underset{\underset{H}{|}}{C}}-H$$
, 26
  24
  incorrect
,

$$H-\underset{\underset{H}{|}}{\overset{\overset{H}{|}}{C}}-\underset{}{\overset{\overset{\displaystyle \overline{O}|}{\|}}{C}}-\overset{\overset{H}{|}}{\underset{\underset{H}{|}}{C}}-H$$
, 24
  24
  correct

21. 3 H 1 × 3 = 3   ,

    1 C 4 × 1 = 4

    1 O 6 × 1 = 6

    1 N 5 × 1 = $\underline{5}$

              18

$$\overline{|\text{O}|}$$
$$\text{H}-\underline{\text{C}}-\overline{\text{N}}-\text{H}$$
$$|$$
$$\text{H}$$

, 20   ,

18

incorrect

$$\overline{\text{O}}|$$
$$\|$$
$$\text{H}-\text{C}-\overline{\text{N}}-\text{H}$$
$$|$$
$$\text{H}$$

, 18   , (alternative structure,

18

correct

$$\overline{|\text{O}|}$$
$$|$$
$$\text{H}-\text{C}=\overline{\text{N}}-\text{H}$$
$$|$$
$$\text{H}$$

, not as good because oxygen has a valence of one)

22. 4 H 1 × 4 = 4   ,

    1 C 4 × 1 = 4

    1 O 6 × 1 = 6

    2 N 5 × 2 = $\underline{10}$

              24

$$\overline{|\text{O}|}$$
$$|$$
$$\text{H}-\overline{\text{N}}-\underline{\text{C}}-\overline{\text{N}}-\text{H}$$
$$|\qquad\quad|$$
$$\text{H}\qquad\ \text{H}$$

, 26   ,

24

incorrect

$$|\overline{\text{O}}$$
$$\|$$
$$\text{H}-\overline{\text{N}}-\text{C}-\overline{\text{N}}-\text{H}$$
$$|\qquad\quad|$$
$$\text{H}\qquad\ \text{H}$$

, 24   , (alternative structure,

24

correct

$$|\overline{\text{O}}|$$
$$|$$
$$\text{H}-\text{N}=\text{C}-\overline{\text{N}}-\text{H}$$
$$|\qquad\qquad|$$
$$\text{H}\qquad\qquad\text{H}$$

, is not as good because oxygen has a valence of one)

23. 12, 14, 2,

$$\overline{\text{O}}|$$
$$\|$$
$$\text{C}-\text{CH}_3$$

24. 1, 1, 5, 8,

$$\text{CH}_2-\text{N}\!\!<^{\text{CH}_3}_{\text{CH}_3}$$, $$\text{CH}_2-\overline{\text{N}}\!\!<^{\text{CH}_3}_{\text{CH}_3}$$, 8, correct

25. 1, 1, 4, 5, 6, 18,

$$\text{H}$$
$$|$$
$$\underline{\text{C}}-\overline{\text{N}}\diagdown\overline{\text{O}}-\text{H}$$

, 20, 2,

$$\text{H}$$
$$|$$
$$\text{C}=\overline{\text{N}}\diagdown\underline{\text{O}}-\text{H}$$

, 4, 3, 2,

$$\text{H}$$
$$|$$
$$\underline{\text{C}}-\overline{\text{N}}=\underline{\text{O}}-\text{H}$$

, 3, 3

26.

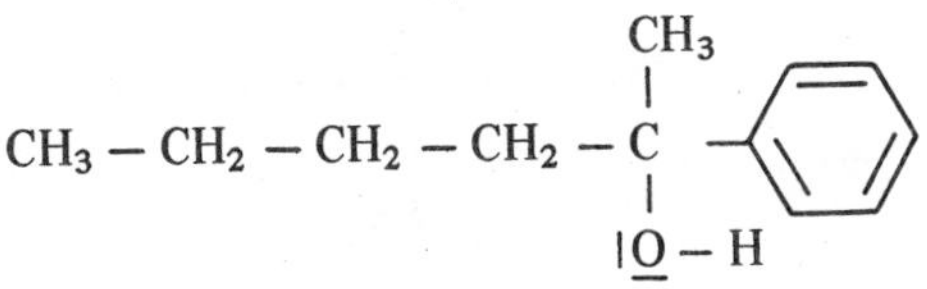

$$CH_3 - CH_2 - CH_2 - CH_2 - \overset{\overset{\displaystyle CH_3}{|}}{\underset{\underset{\displaystyle \underline{O} - H}{|}}{C}}\text{—}(phenyl)$$

27.

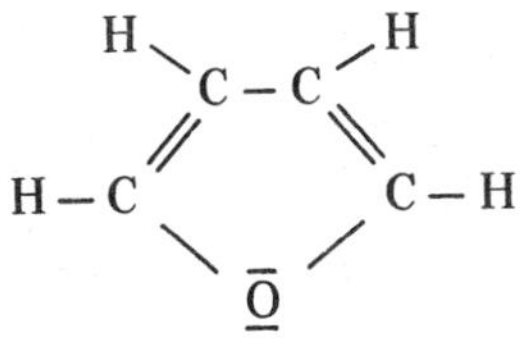

Five-membered ring:
H–C=C–H (top carbons each bearing H), H–C and C–H lower carbons, with $\underline{O}$ at the bottom.

28.

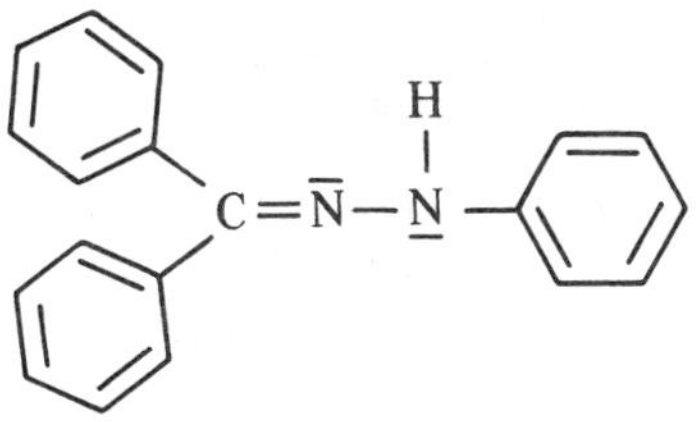

$(phenyl)(phenyl)C=\overline{N}-\underset{\underset{\displaystyle}{}}{\overset{\overset{\displaystyle H}{|}}{N}}-(phenyl)$

29.

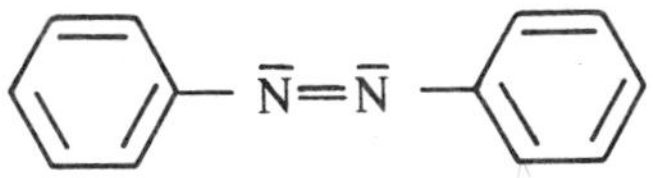

$(phenyl)-\overline{N}=\overline{N}-(phenyl)$

30.

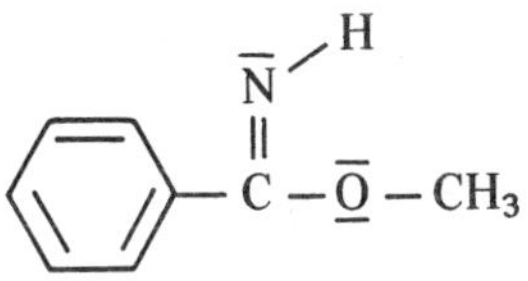

$(phenyl)-\underset{}{\overset{\overset{\displaystyle \overline{N}-H}{||}}{C}}-\overline{O}-CH_3$

31.

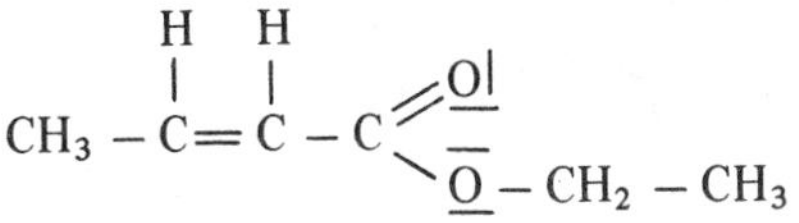

$$CH_3 - \overset{\overset{\displaystyle H}{|}}{C}=\overset{\overset{\displaystyle H}{|}}{C} - C\overset{\diagup \underline{O}|}{\underset{\diagdown \overline{O} - CH_2 - CH_3}{}}$$

32.

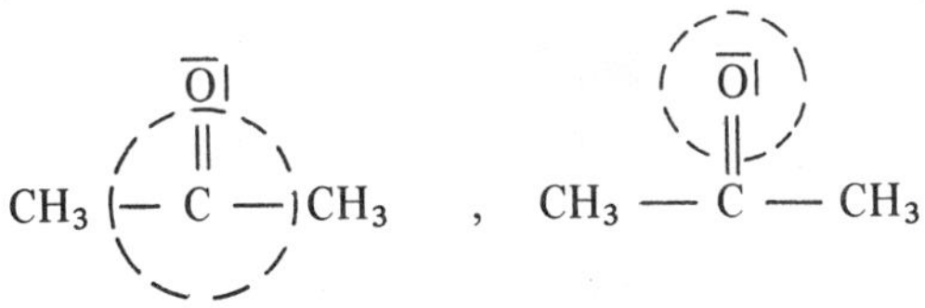

$CH_3 \overset{\overline{O}|}{\underset{||}{(-\ C\ -)}} CH_3$, $CH_3 - \overset{\overline{O}|}{\underset{||}{C}} - CH_3$

33.

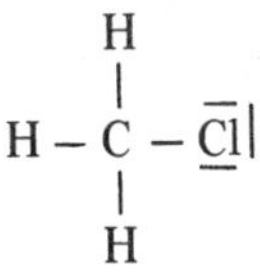

$$H - \overset{\overset{\displaystyle H}{|}}{\underset{\underset{\displaystyle H}{|}}{C}} - \overline{\underline{Cl}}| \quad , \quad 4, IV$$

34. 1, 1, 3, VII, zero

35. 4, 1, 4, IV, zero

36. 2, 2, 6, VI, zero

37. 1, 5, 6, 18, [Ph–N with two –|Ō| groups] , 20, [Ph–N with =O| and –Ō| groups] , 4, 1, 4, V, 5

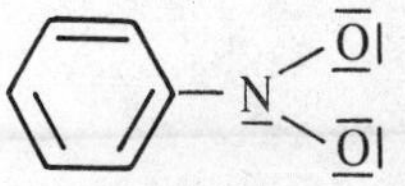

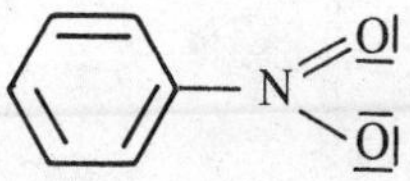

38. 2, 2, 6, VI, zero, 3, 1, 7, −1

39.

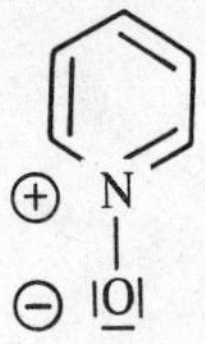

[pyridinium N⊕ with –|Ō|⊖ structure]

40.

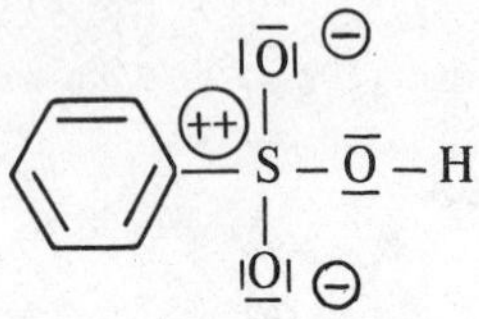

[Ph–S(⊕⊕) with two |Ō|⊖ groups and –Ō–H]

41.

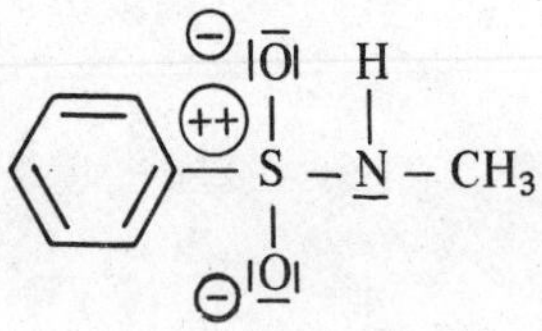

[Ph–S(⊕⊕) with two |Ō|⊖ groups and –N(H)–CH₃]

42.

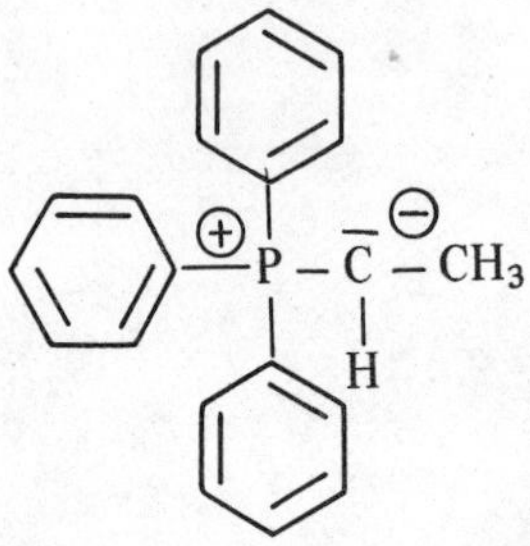

[(Ph)₃P⊕–C⊖(H)–CH₃]

43.

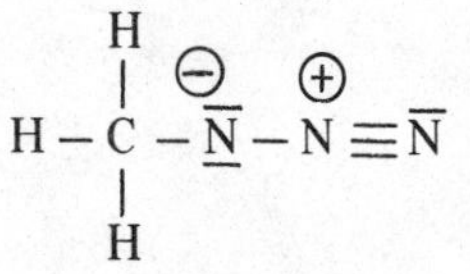

$$H–C(H)(H)–\bar{N}^{\ominus}–N^{\oplus}\equiv\bar{N}$$

44.

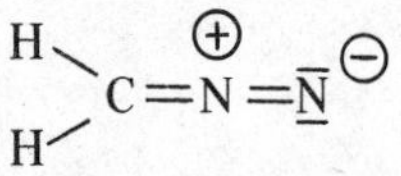

$$\underset{H}{\overset{H}{>}}C=N^{\oplus}=\bar{N}^{\ominus}$$

45.

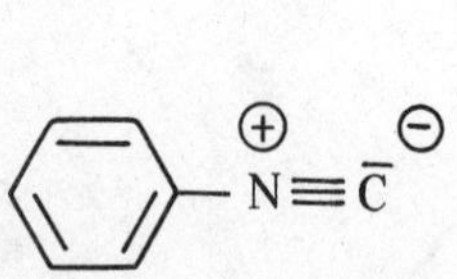

[Ph–N⊕≡C̄⊖]

46.

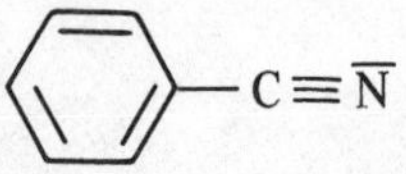

[Ph–C≡N̄] , (formal charge is zero on all atoms)

47.

$$CH_3 - \overset{\overset{CH_3}{|}}{\underset{\underset{CH_3}{|}}{\overset{\oplus}{N}}} - \overline{\underline{O}}| \ ^{\ominus}$$

48.

$$CH_3 \overset{\oplus}{-} \underset{}{\overset{\overset{|\overline{O}| \ ^{\ominus}}{|}}{\underline{S}}} - CH_3$$

49. 3, 1, 3, IV, 4, +1, 4, 8, −1

50.

$$CH_3 - CH_2 - \overset{\overset{H}{|}}{\underset{\underset{H}{|}}{C}} \quad , \ 3, 1, 3, +1, \quad CH_3 - CH_2 - \overset{\overset{H}{|}}{\underset{\underset{H}{|}}{C}}{}^{\oplus}$$

51.

$$CH_3 - \overset{\overset{H}{|}}{\underset{\underset{CH_3}{|}}{C}} \quad 3, 3, +1, \ CH_3 - \overset{\overset{H}{|}}{\underset{\underset{CH_3}{|}}{C}}{}^{\oplus}$$

52.

— H , 3, 3, +1, ${}^{\oplus}$ H

53. 3, 1, 5, VI, +1, $CH_3 - \overset{\oplus}{\underset{\underset{H}{|}}{\overline{O}}} H$

54. $CH_3 - CH_2 - \underset{\underset{H}{|}}{\overline{O}} - CH_2 - CH_3$, 3, 1, 5, +1, $CH_3 - CH_2 - \underset{\underset{H}{|}}{\overset{\oplus}{\overline{O}}} CH_2 - CH_3$

55.

, 3, 1, +1,

56.

$$CH_3 - \underset{\underset{H}{|}}{\overset{\overset{H}{|}}{N}} - H \quad , \ 4, 1, 4, V, +1, \quad CH_3 - \underset{\underset{H}{|}}{\overset{\overset{H}{|}}{\overset{\oplus}{N}}} H$$

57.

$$CH_3 - CH_2 - \underset{\underset{H}{|}}{\overset{\overset{H}{|}}{N}} - CH_2 - CH_3 \ , \ 4, 4, +1, \ CH_3 - CH_2 - \underset{\underset{H}{|}}{\overset{\overset{H}{|}}{\overset{\oplus}{N}}} CH_2 - CH_3$$

58,

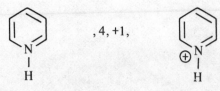

, 4, +1,

59. 3, 1, 5, IV, +1

60.

$$CH_3 - CH_2 - CH_2 - \overset{\displaystyle H}{\underset{\displaystyle H}{C}} - \quad , \quad 3, 1, 5, -1, \quad CH_3 - CH_2 - CH_2 - \overset{\displaystyle H}{\underset{\displaystyle H}{C}} \overset{\ominus}{|}$$

61.

$$CH_3 - \underset{\displaystyle CH_3}{CH} - \overset{\displaystyle H}{\underset{\displaystyle H}{C}} - \quad , \quad 3, 1, 5, \quad CH_3 - \underset{\displaystyle CH_3}{CH} - \overset{\displaystyle H}{\underset{\displaystyle H}{C}} \overset{\ominus}{|}$$

62.

⬡$- \overset{\displaystyle H}{\underset{\displaystyle H}{C}} -$, 3, 1, −1, ⬡$- \overset{\displaystyle H}{\underset{\displaystyle H}{C}} \overset{\ominus}{|}$

63. 1, 3, 7, VI, −1, $CH_3 - CH_2 - \overline{\underline{O}}|\,^{\ominus}$

64.

$$CH_3 - \underset{\displaystyle CH_3}{\overset{\displaystyle CH_3}{C}} - \overline{\underline{O}}| \quad , \quad 1, 3, 7, -1, \quad CH_3 - \underset{\displaystyle CH_3}{\overset{\displaystyle CH_3}{C}} - \overline{\underline{O}}|\,^{\ominus}$$

65. $CH_3 - \overline{\underline{N}} - H$, 2, 2, 6, V, −1, $CH_3 - \overline{\underline{N}}\,^{\ominus}H$

66.

⬡$- \overline{\underline{N}} - H$, 6, −1, ⬡$- \overline{\underline{N}}\,^{\ominus}H$

RESONANCE STRUCTURES

Correct Lewis structures are very helpful in understanding the chemical and physical properties of organic molecules. As will be seen in Chapter 3 of this text they are essential to writing the mechanisms of organic reactions. As helpful as they are, single Lewis structures do not always accurately describe an organic compound.

By this time you should be acquainted with the resonance method. The resonance method, while still preserving the useful features of the Lewis structures, is a procedure used to describe accurately a molecule for which one single Lewis structure is not sufficient. The resonance method describes the true structure of a molecule as a hybrid of several Lewis structures. These Lewis structures are called resonance or contributing structures. It is *essential* to understand that there is only *one* structure for the actual molecule. That structure is not written down but takes its character from the resonance structures. Resonance structures have no discrete existence of their own but, taken in combination, describe the true structure of the molecule.

The resonance method consists of writing down all the possible resonance structures and making a judgment about which of the resonance structures will make important contributions to the hybrid. In order to do that, one *must be able* to write down resonance structures.

There are several rules to which acceptable resonance structures for a compound must conform. First, the relative positions of all atoms in all resonance structures for a single compound must be the same. Second, all resonance structures for a single compound must have the same number of paired and unpaired electrons. It follows from this rule that the algebraic sum of formal charge on all resonance structures for a single compound must be the same. Third, the important resonance structures will have comparable energies.[1]

While these rules are important they are not awfully helpful to the student faced with the task of writing resonance structures. This Chapter will present a method by which one can set about

---

[1] That is, any resonance structure which has an energy substantially higher than the rest must be discarded. The energy of a particular structure depends on several things (charge distribution, the octet rule, steric strain, etc.). Judging the relative energies of a series of structures requires an intuitive sense which is only developed through experience. This Chapter concentrates solely on how to move electrons to generate a series of resonance structures.

writing resonance structures by starting with one Lewis structure and "pushing electrons" to generate new resonance structures. To do that one must find the proper combination of "pushable electrons" and places to which electrons can be pushed (receptors).

In Lewis structures the pushable electron pairs are the unshared (n) electron pairs and the pi electron pairs in multiple bonds.[2]

Receptors can be: (1) atoms with a formal positive charge: (2) atoms which can tolerate a formal negative charge: (3) atoms which possess pushable electrons themselves.

SIMPLE IONS

CATIONS

One Lewis structure for the allyl cation is

This structure contains a pair of pushable electrons, namely the pi electrons in the double bond between C_2 and C_3. The structure also contains a positively charged carbon atom at C_1 which can act as a receptor. A new resonance structure can be generated by "pushing" (signified by ⤵) the electrons to the receptor. Thus,

By pushing electrons to the receptor, the positive charge has been neutralized, but a new positive charge has been generated at C_3 since electrons have been pushed away leaving only six electrons around C_3, three of which "belong" to C_3. Structure *1* can be regenerated from *2* by pushing the pi electrons between C_1 and C_2 toward the positively charged carbon C_3. Structures *1* and *2* are equivalent but not identical. In the resonance notation this is written:

$$H_2C = CH - \overset{\oplus}{C}H_2 \longleftrightarrow H_2\overset{\oplus}{C} - CH = CH_2 .$$

(See footnote 3.)

---

[2]Only under unusual and controversial circumstances are sigma electrons pushed to generate resonance structures.

[3]At this point the reader should check paragraph 4 to be sure that these two resonance structures obey the rules set out there. The assignment of formal charge also should be checked.

1. One Lewis structure for the 3-methylallyl cation is $CH_3-CH=CH-CH_2^{\oplus}$. A new resonance structure can be generated by pushing the pi electrons to the receptor. Thus,

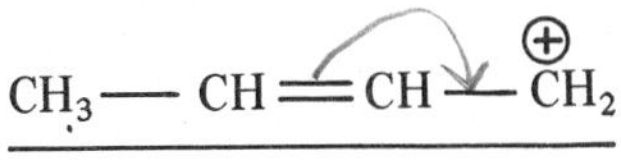

$$CH_3 — CH = CH \quad CH_2^{\oplus}$$

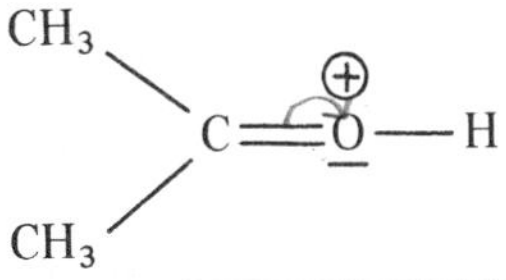

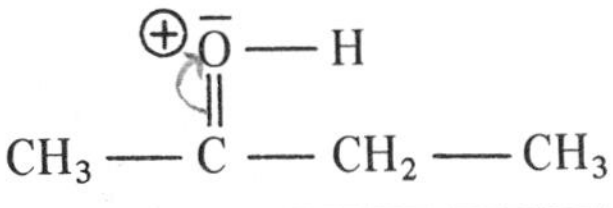

<u>supply arrow</u>

generates

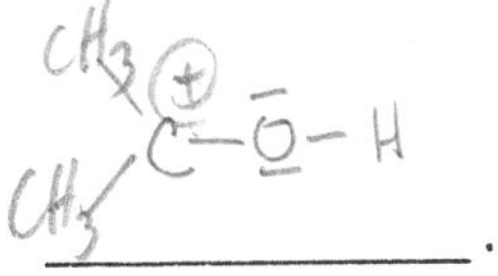

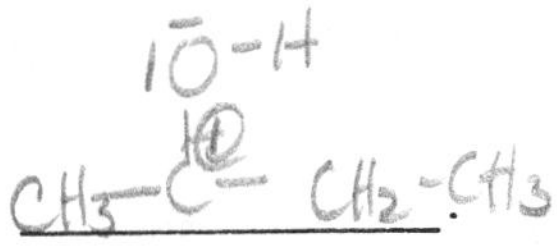

$CH_3 - \overset{\oplus}{C}H - CH = CH_2$

(See footnote 4.)

2. A second resonance structure for the 3-cyclopentenyl cation can be generated. Thus,

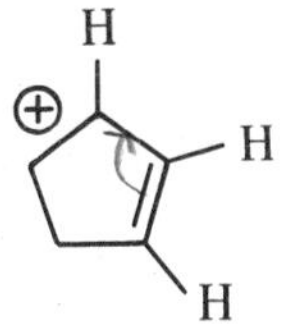

gives

<u>supply arrow</u>

3. One structure for the conjugate acid of acetone is

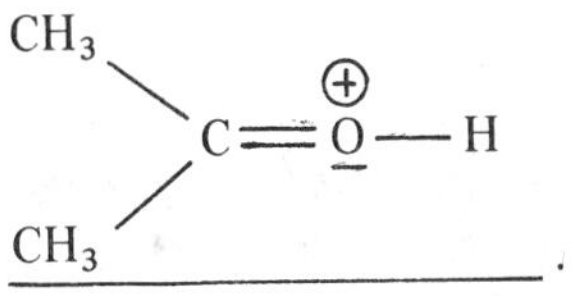

The __π__ electrons in the carbon-oxygen double bond are pushable electrons and the __O__ atom is a receptor. Thus,

generates

<u>supply arrow</u>

4. Similarly, a resonance structure for the conjugate acid of 2-butanone can be written. Thus,

generates

<u>supply arrow</u>

---

[4] It is very important that these arrows indicate precisely *what* electrons are being pushed *where*. Therefore, after doing these exercises check the answers carefully to see that the arrows have been inserted properly.

5. A second resonance structure for protonated cycloheptanone is produced by

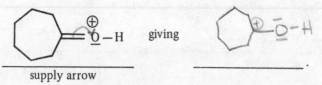

supply arrow   giving

6. Pairs of unshared electrons can be pushed. One Lewis structure for the methoxymethyl cation is $CH_3-\bar{O}-CH_2^{\oplus}$. The structure contains a pair of pushable electrons, namely the _unshared_ electrons on the ___O___ atom. The structure also contains a positively charged ___C___ atom which can act as a _receptor_. A second resonance structure can be generated by pushing the n electrons to the receptor. Thus,

$$CH_3 - \bar{O} \curvearrowright CH_2^{\oplus}$$

supply arrow   generates $CH_3 - \overset{\oplus}{O} = CH_2$

It is not possible to push the n electrons toward the other carbon because it is not a receptor.

7. One structure for the acetoxonium ion is

$$CH_3 - \overset{\oplus}{C} = \bar{O}$$
$$(3)$$

Clearly, the receptor is the positively charged ___C___ atom. However, there are available two different kinds of pushable electrons, namely, pi electrons in the carbon-oxygen double bond or n electrons on the oxygen atom. The proper choice in this case is dictated by the following. In structure *3* the carbon atom possesses a formal positive charge and also has only six electrons in its outer shell (it lacks a stable octet of electrons). If the pi electrons are pushed, namely,

$$CH_3 - \overset{\oplus}{C} \overset{\curvearrowleft}{=} \bar{O} \longleftrightarrow CH_3 - \bar{C} - \bar{O}^{\oplus}, \text{ very unstable}$$
$$(4)$$

a structure (*4*) is obtained in which the oxygen possesses a formal positive charge but, in addition, both the oxygen *and* the carbon atom lack a stable octet. This structure will be very unstable. Structure *4*, despite the fact that it can be generated by properly pushing electrons, is not included in the resonance hybrid for the acetoxonium ion. If, on the other hand, the n electrons on the oxygen are pushed, a more acceptable structure is obtained, namely,

$$CH_3 - \overset{\oplus}{C} \overset{\curvearrowleft}{=} \bar{O} \longleftrightarrow CH_3 - C \equiv \overset{\oplus}{O}$$
$$(5)$$

In structure *5* the oxygen atom possesses a formal positive charge and both the carbon and the oxygen atom have a stable octet. Structure *5* is included in the resonance hybrid.[5]

---

[5] One might wonder why structure *3* which contains one atom lacking a stable octet is considered to have comparable energy to *5* in which all atoms possess a stable octet. The discrepancy in energy introduced by this factor is offset partly by the fact that carbon, being less electronegative than oxygen, is better able to tolerate the positive charge. This tends to stabilize *3* with respect to *5*.

8. Another ion of this type is

$$CH_3 - CH - \overset{\oplus}{C} = \underline{O}$$

(with CH_3 below the CH)

supply arrow

which gives the resonance structure

$$CH_3 - CH - C \equiv \underline{O}^{\oplus}$$

(with CH_3 below the CH).

* * * * *

It is important to recognize opportunities to push electrons and generate new resonance structures. It is also important to recognize those structures in which one *cannot* push electrons. That is, in order to be able to generate one or more resonance structures, a Lewis structure must have (1) pushable electrons, (2) a receptor, and (3) the receptor must be *next to* the pushable electrons.

9. There are no important resonance structures for the isopropyl cation,

$$H_3C - \overset{\oplus}{C}H - CH_3 \ ,$$

because there are no *pushable electrons* in the structure. There are no important resonance structures for dimethyl ether,

$$H_3C - \overline{O} - CH_3 \ ,$$

because, although there are pushable (n) electrons on the oxygen atom, there is no *receptor*. There are no important resonance structures for the 5-pentenyl cation,

$$H_2C = CH - CH_2 - CH_2 - \overset{\oplus}{C}H_2 \ ,$$

because the pushable electrons and the receptor are separated by two methylene groups. Thus, the electrons have no way to get to the receptor.

Exercises

In this exercise one Lewis structure is provided. In some cases one more resonance structure can be generated by pushing electrons. In other cases no additional structures can be generated.

10.

$$\begin{array}{c} CH_3 \\ \diagdown \\ C = CH - \overset{\oplus}{C}H - CH_3 \\ \diagup \\ CH_3 \end{array} \longleftrightarrow \begin{array}{c} CH_3 \\ \overset{\oplus}{C} - CH = CH - CH_3 \\ CH_3 \end{array}$$

11.

12.

13.

14.

15.

16.

17.

ANIONS

One Lewis structure for the acetate ion is

This structure contains several pairs of pushable electrons. Since the object of writing resonance structures is to show delocalization of charge, it is reasonable that electrons should be pushed *away* from a center of negative charge. Pushing a pair of n electrons on the negatively charged oxygen toward the carbonyl carbon would give

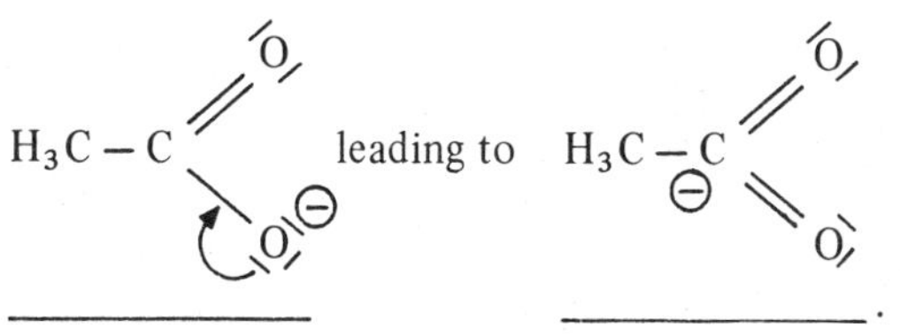

leading to

_____   _____ .   (See footnote 6.)

This, however, gives the intolerable situation of having ten valence electrons around the carboxyl carbon. The situation can be relieved by pushing the pi electrons of the original carbon-oxygen double bond toward the oxygen atom which can tolerate the negative charge. Thus,

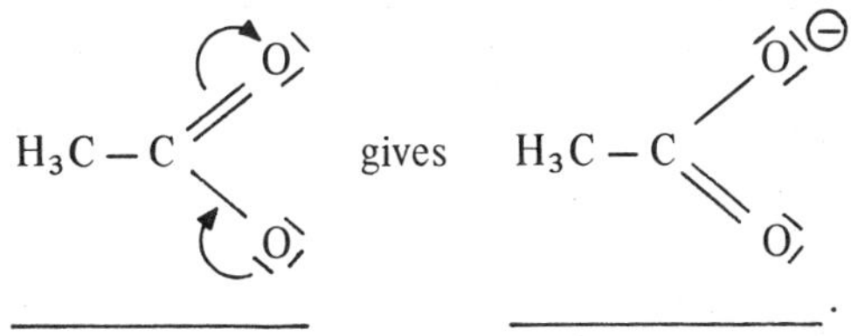

gives

_____   _____ .

18. The cyclohexane carboxylate anion has a Lewis structure

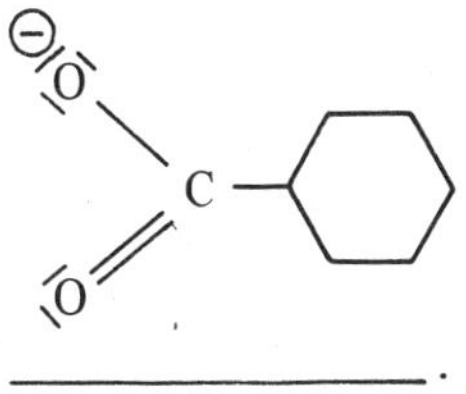

_____ .

Pushing a pair of n electrons away from the negatively charged oxygen atom and, at the same time, pushing a pair of pi electrons toward the other oxygen will generate a second resonance structure. Thus,

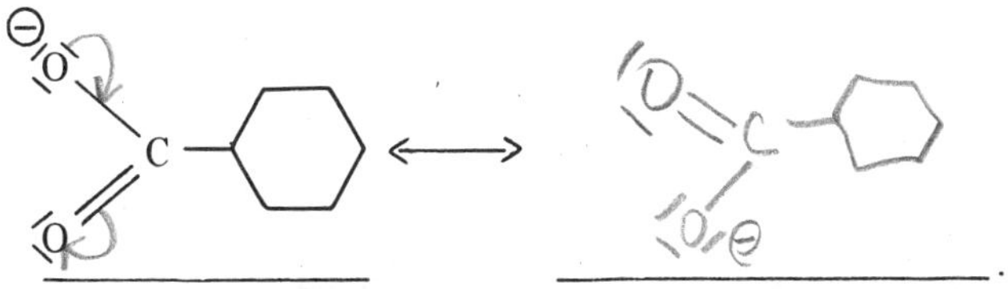

⟷

supply arrows   _____ .

19. One Lewis structure for the enolate anion of acetaldehyde is

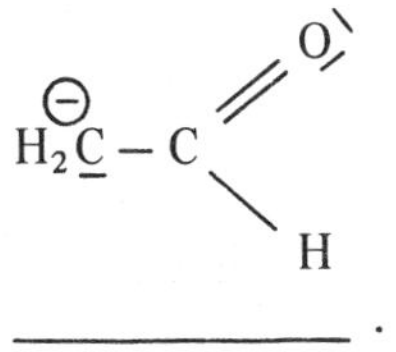

_____ .

Pushing the pair of unshared electrons on the carbon atom away from the center of negative

---

[6] This is a horrible structure used only this once for pedagogical purposes. You should erase it from your memory immediately!

charge and pushing the pi electrons of the carbon-oxygen double bond to the oxygen atom generates a second resonance structure. Thus,

$$H_2\overset{\ominus}{C} - C \overset{O}{\underset{H}{\diagup}} \qquad \text{gives} \qquad H_2C = C \overset{\ominus O}{\underset{H}{\diagup}}$$

_____
supply arrows   _____

20. The allyl anion is a resonance hybrid. One of the two equivalent resonance structures is

$$\overset{\ominus}{CH_2} - CH = CH_2 \quad .$$

Delocalization of the n electrons on the negatively charged carbon atom and simultaneous delocalization of the pi electrons to the other terminal carbon atom generates the other structure. Thus,

$$\overset{\ominus}{CH_2} - CH = CH_2 \longleftrightarrow CH_2 = CH - \overset{-\ominus}{CH_2}$$

_____
supply arrows   _____ .

21. The acetonitrile anion provides a slight variation on this theme. Thus, one pair of pi electrons in a triple bond is pushed.

$$\overset{\ominus}{CH_2} - C \equiv \underline{N} \longleftrightarrow CH_2 = C = \bar{\underline{N}}^{\ominus}$$

_____
supply arrows   _____ .

*   *   *   *   *

Here are several common errors and misconceptions which appear frequently in folks' attempts to write resonance structures:

(1) Always push *electrons,* never push positive charges. Remember that the arrows used in generating resonance structures indicate how the electrons are moving. A structure such as

$$CH_2 = CH - \overset{\oplus}{CH_2}$$

is incorrect.

(2) Always push electrons away from centers of negative charge and toward centers of positive charge. The resonance method depends on delocalizing charge. Electrons which have negative charge, therefore, must be pushed away from centers of relatively high electron density and toward centers of relatively low electron density.

$$CH_2 = CH - \overset{\oplus}{CH_2} \qquad\qquad CH_2 = CH - \overset{\oplus}{CH_2}$$

correct   incorrect!

$$CH_2 = CH - \bar{C}H_2^{\ominus} \qquad CH_2 = CH - \bar{C}H_2^{\ominus}$$

correct   incorrect!

Exercises

In these exercises one Lewis structure is provided. In some cases one more resonance structure can be written. In other cases there are no additional resonance structures.

22.

23.

24.

25.

26.

27.

28.

BENZENE AND BENZENOID AROMATIC COMPOUNDS

The best known example of a resonance hybrid is benzene. Benzene has a Lewis structure

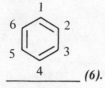

_(6)._

This structure contains three pairs of pushable electrons. It is expedient, however, to consider only one pair, say the pair of pi electrons between C_1 and C_2 as the pushable electrons and the others as being associated with receptors.

29. Drawing an arrow pushing the C_1-C_2 pi electrons toward C_3 would result in the unacceptable situation of having ten electrons around C_3. The situation is relieved by pushing the C_3-C_4 pi electrons toward C_5 giving

This presents C_5 with the same dilemma that C_3 had a moment ago. By pushing the C_5-C_6 pi electrons toward C_1 the dilemma is solved since C_1 is missing the pair of pushable pi electrons that were used to begin this process. Thus,

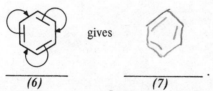

Structures _6_ and _7_ are referred to as Kekulé[7] structures. Whenever a benzene ring appears in a compound the two Kekulé structures should be the first two resonance structures written down.[8]

---

[7]August Kekulé (1829 to 1896) proposed and proved this structure for benzene in 1865. He recognized at the time that a single structure did not account for certain properties of benzene and proposed, not too convincingly, a dynamic equilibrium between the two equivalent but not identical structures. The resonance theory (1935) resolved this problem.

[8]Several shorthand notations which imply the two Kekulé structures are used by organic chemists. They are:

$$\bigcirc\!\!\!\!\!\bigcirc - \quad , \quad C_6H_5 - , \quad Ph - , \quad and \quad \Phi - .$$

Each of these can be used to indicate the phenyl group. Thus, toluene can be written:

$$\bigcirc\!\!\!\!\!\bigcirc - CH_3 \, , \quad C_6H_5 - CH_3 \, , \quad Ph - CH_3 \, , \quad \Phi - CH_3$$

or

$$CH_3 \qquad\qquad CH_3$$

$$\bigcirc\!\!\!\!\!\bigcirc \longleftrightarrow \bigcirc\!\!\!\!\!\bigcirc$$

30. A second resonance structure for *ortho*-xylene can be generated. Thus,

supply arrows

31. When more than one benzene ring is present in the same molecule, the number of possible resonance structures is increased. In diphenylmethanol,

a second resonance structure can be generated by pushing electrons in the ring on the right and leaving the ring on the left undisturbed. Thus,

Conversely, pushing electrons in the ring on the left and leaving the right undisturbed gives another structure. Thus,

supply arrows

Finally, pushing electrons on both rings gives a fourth resonance structure. Thus,

supply arrows

The complete resonance notation for diphenylmethanol is:

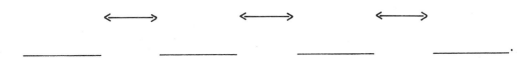

*   *   *   *   *

Compounds containing benzene rings which have two carbon atoms in common are called "fused" aromatic compounds. Writing resonance structures for fused aromatic compounds is done in a way similar to that described for diphenylmethanol. That is, electrons in one ring are pushed and the rest of the molecule is left undisturbed.

32. One Lewis structure for naphthalene is

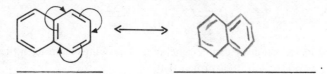

Pushing electrons in the right ring and leaving the left alone gives:

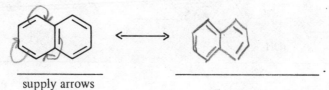

Pushing electrons in the left ring and leaving the right alone gives:

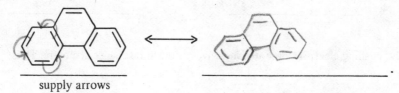

supply arrows

Note that one cannot push electrons in adjacent fused rings at the same time because one pair of pi electrons is held in common between the two.

33. Phenanthrene contains three fused rings and has five acceptable resonance structures. They can be generated as follows:

(a) Push electrons in the left ring.

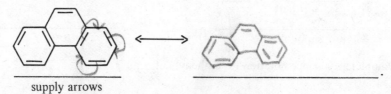

supply arrows

(b) Push electrons in the right ring.

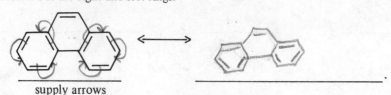

supply arrows

(c) Push electrons in the right and left rings.

supply arrows

(d) Push electrons in the central ring.

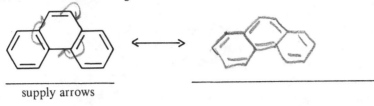

_____   _____ .

supply arrows

*   *   *   *   *

Writing resonance structures for fused aromatic compounds is an area particularly rich in opportunities for incorrect structures. After all resonance structures for fused aromatic compounds are written down, check for and remove:

(1) Any with ten electrons around carbon, e.g.,

(2) Any structures which do not have a continuous system of alternating single and double bonds, e.g.,

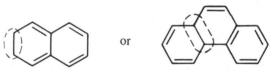

(3) Any structures which are identical with others in the set, e.g.,

is identical to

Exercises

In these exercises one Lewis structure of an aromatic compound is given along with the total number (including the one provided) of possible structures. Write the other structures.

34. Ethylbenzene (2)

CH₂ — CH₃

35. *p*-xylene (2)

CH₃

CH₃

36. Anthracene (4)

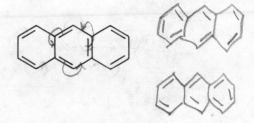

MORE COMPLICATED IONS

37. Very often more than two resonance structures can be written for an ion. One Lewis structure for the phenoxide ion is

(8)

The structure contains a pair of pushable electrons, namely, the n electrons on the negatively charged oxygen atom. The structure also contains a receptor, C_1, from which a pair of pi electrons can be pushed to C_2. This is shown as

which generates

(9)

Structure **9** in its turn can be used to generate another resonance structure by pushing the unshared electrons at C_2 toward C_3 as the C_3-C_4 pi electrons are pushed to C_4. Thus,

supply arrows   generates   *(10)*

A final structure, equivalent to but not identical to **9** can be arrived at by pushing the unshared pair at C_4 toward C_5 and moving the C_5-C_6 pi electrons to C_6. Thus,

supply arrows   generates   *(11)*

The complete resonance method designation for phenoxide ion, including both Kekulé forms of the first structure is: (Try to complete this without referring back to the structures you have just written.)

38. One Lewis structure for the cyclopentadienide anion is

$$(12)$$

Four additional resonance structures can be written. The pair of unshared electrons at C_1 is pushed toward C_2 and the pair of pi electrons between C_2 and C_3 is pushed toward C_3.

$$(12) \longleftrightarrow (13)$$

In structure *13* there is a pair of electrons at C_3 and double bonds at C_4-C_5 and C_1-C_2. The unshared pair at C_3 is pushed toward C_4 and the pair of pi electrons at C_4-C_5 is pushed toward C_5.

supply arrows
$$(13) \longleftrightarrow (14)$$

This process can be repeated twice more to generate equivalent, but not identical, structures.

$$(14) \longleftrightarrow (15)$$

$$(15) \longleftrightarrow (16)$$

A similar operation on *16* regenerates *12*.

39. There are five acceptable resonance structures for the benzyl cation,

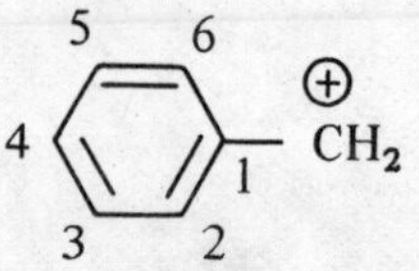

(17)

First, the other Kekulé structure,

(18)

Then, a pair of pi electrons from the ring can be pushed toward the positively charged carbon atom.

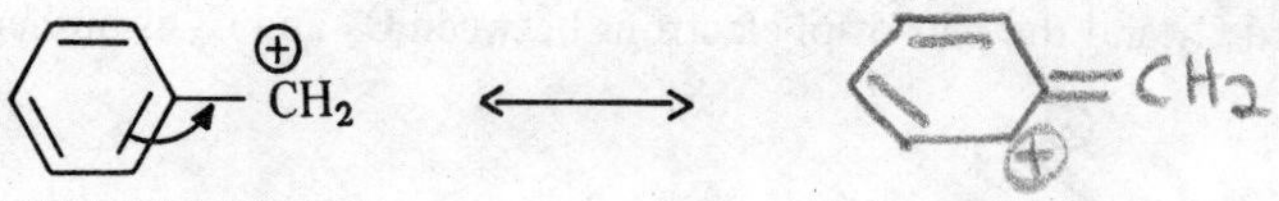

(17)   *(19)*

Structure *19* becomes *20* by pushing the C_3-C_4 pi electrons.

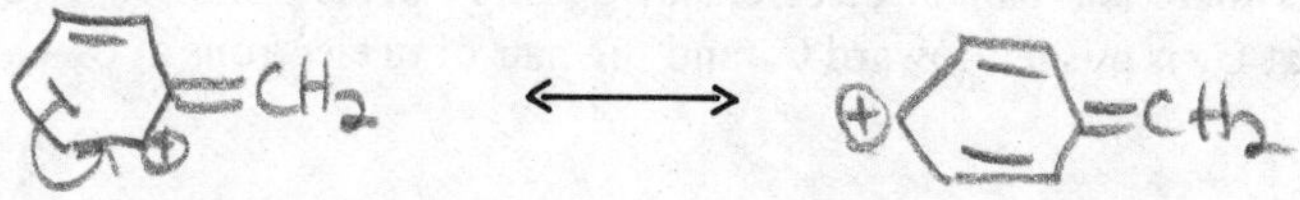

(19)   *(20)*

A similar operation on *20* generates *21* which is equivalent, but not identical to *19*.

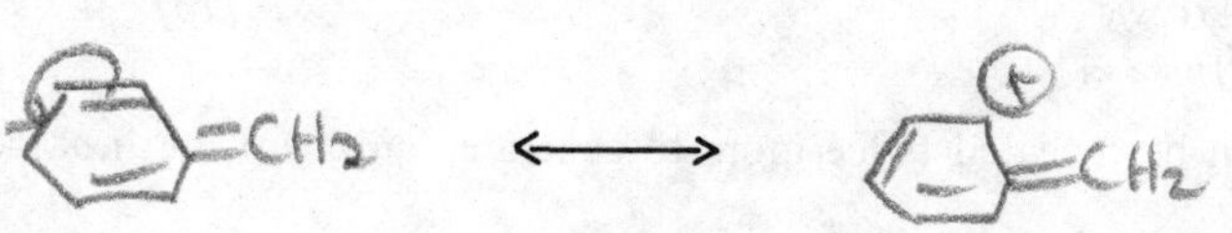

(20)   *(21)*

40. As long as pushable electrons and receptors are available one can continue to write new resonance structures. For example, in the bromination of aniline the following intermediate appears,

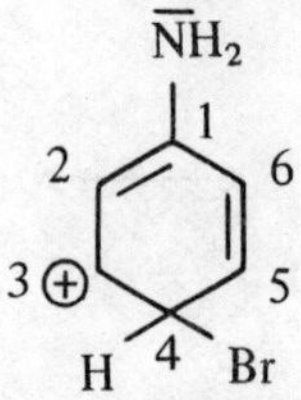

(22)

The pair of pi electrons between C_1 and C_2 can be pushed toward the positively charged C_3 which is a receptor. Thus,

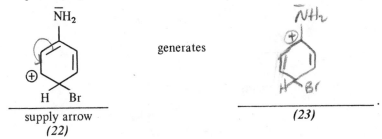

supply arrow
(22)

generates

(23)

In this new structure the same opportunity presents itself, i.e., to push the pair of pi electrons between C_5 and C_6 to the positively charged carbon at C_1. Thus,

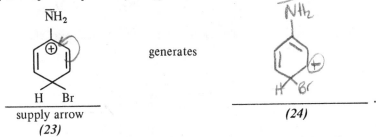

supply arrow
(23)

generates

(24)

In structure *23* there is another pair of pushable electrons next to the receptor, namely, the unshared pair on the nitrogen atom and

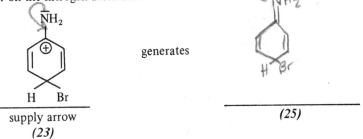

supply arrow
(23)

generates

(25)

The complete resonance method notation for this intermediate is: (Don't look back.)

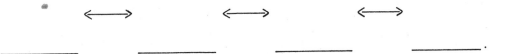

41. An intermediate in the bromination of styrene is

$$\overset{\oplus}{\underset{Br}{\overset{H}{\underset{5}{\overset{3}{\bigtimes}}}}}\quad CH = CH_2 .$$

(26)

The pair of electrons between C_1 and C_2 can be pushed toward C_3.

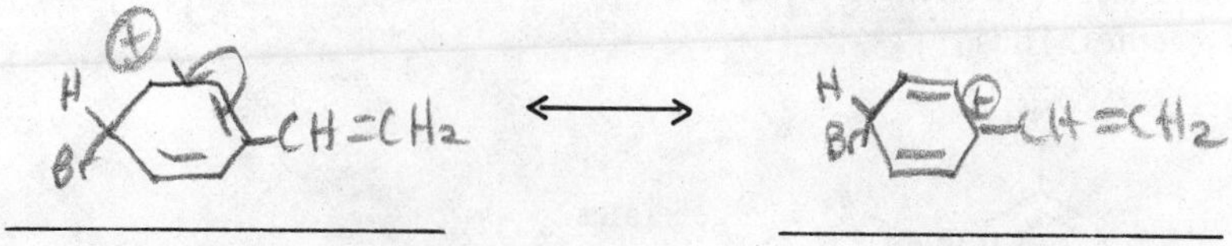

(26)   (27)

In *27* the same opportunity presents itself.

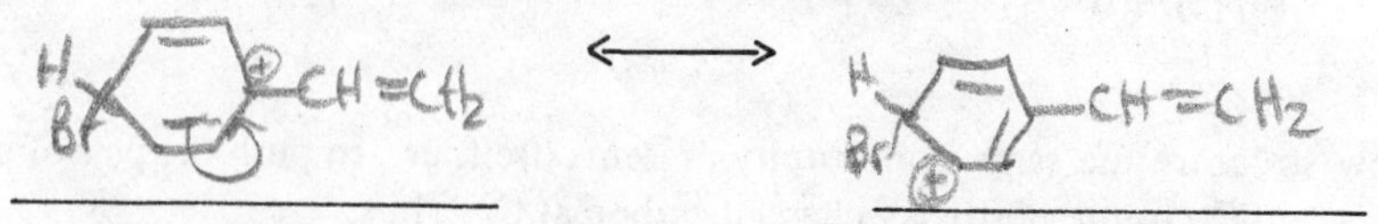

(27)   (28)

In *27* there is another pair of pushable electrons, namely, the pair of pi electrons in the double bond outside the benzene ring.

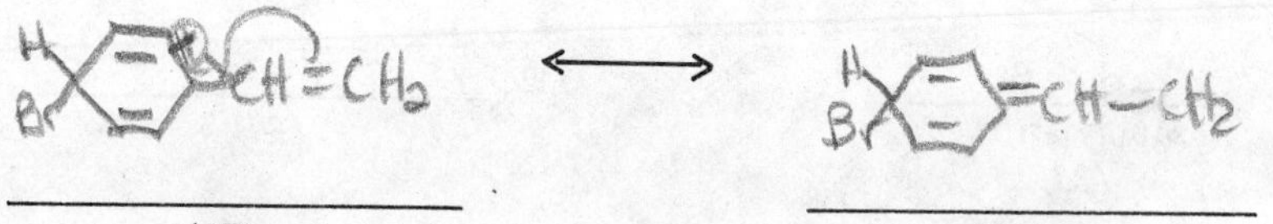

(27)   (29)

Exercises

One Lewis structure is provided along with the number of possible structures (including the one provided). Write the other structures.

42. (3)

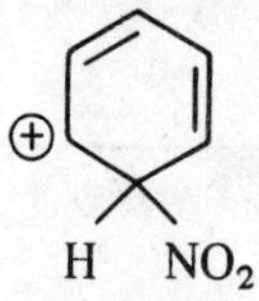

H   NO$_2$

43. (3)

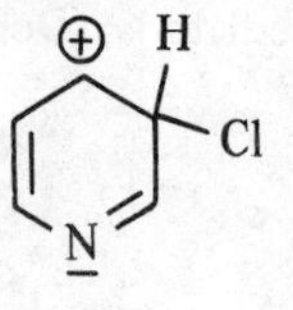

44. (7)

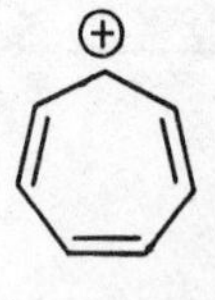

45. (3)

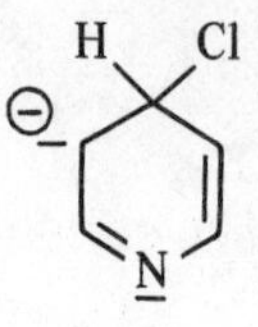

46. (4)

MOLECULES HAVING RESONANCE STRUCTURES WITH CHARGE SEPARATION

So far in this Chapter the resonance structures which have been generated contained the same formal charge distribution as the original structures. These resonance structures are significant because the energies of the various structures are similar and, thus, each structure tends to make an important contribution to the hybrid.

In many cases, however, molecules for which there is a Lewis structure with no formal charge separation also have resonance structures with charge separation. These structures make smaller, albeit finite, contributions to the hybrid.

The Lewis structure for formaldehyde is

Of the two atoms, carbon and oxygen, which are sharing the pi electrons of the carbonyl bond, oxygen is the more electronegative. Therefore, it can act as a receptor. Pushing the pi electrons to the oxygen atom generates a new resonance structure. Thus,

generates   (See footnote 9.)

---

[9]The introduction of charge separation into a resonance structure usually increases the energy of that structure relative to one in which no separation of charge appears. The uncharged structure makes a substantially greater contribution to the hybrid. However, proposing that the charged structure makes a smaller but finite contribution emphasizes the electrophilic nature of a carbonyl carbon atom and the nucleophilic nature of the carbonyl oxygen atom. An alternative structure in which the pi electrons are pushed toward the carbon atom, i.e.,

is not considered because it makes no sense physically to push electrons away from the more electronegative atom.

47. One Lewis structure for acrolein (propenal) is

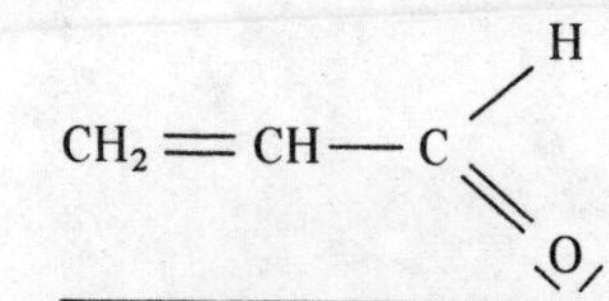

$$CH_2 = CH - C \overset{H}{\underset{O}{}}.$$

Pushing the pi electrons of the carbonyl bond toward the oxygen atom will generate a second resonance structure. Thus,

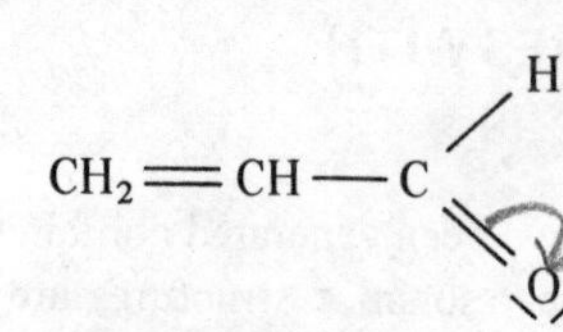

generates

supply arrow

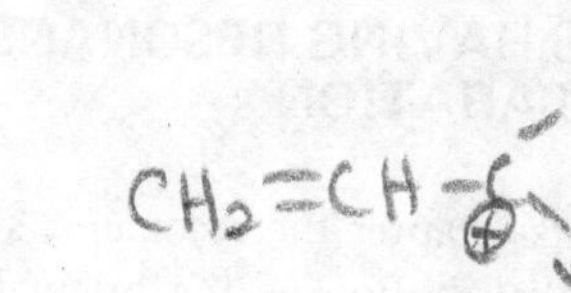

This second structure has a pair of pushable electrons (viz., the pi electrons of the carbon-carbon double bond) next to a receptor, the carbonyl carbon atom which possesses a formal positive charge. Thus,

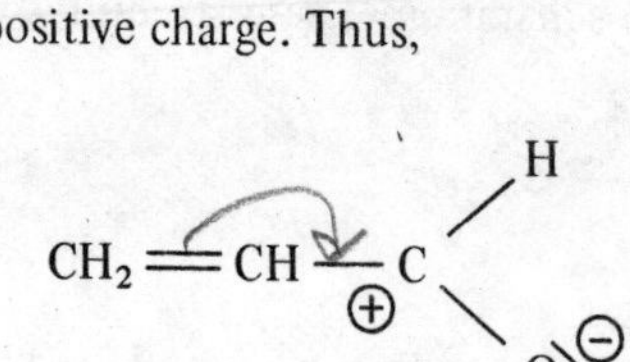

gives

supply arrow

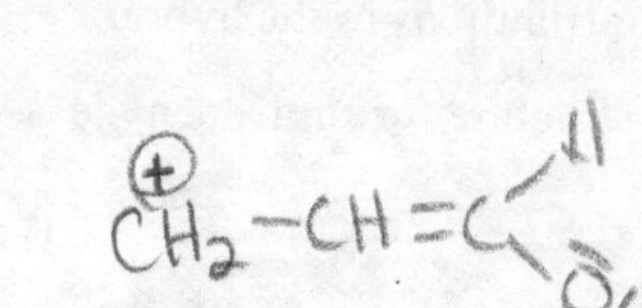

The resonance method notation for acrolein is: (Don't look back.)

$$\longleftrightarrow \qquad \longleftrightarrow$$

48. One Lewis structure for N-methylacetamide is

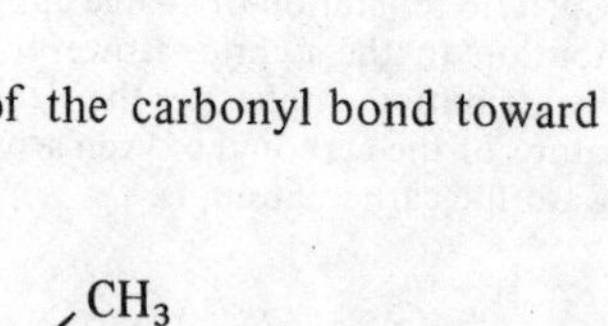

$$CH_3 - \overset{\overset{|\overline{O}|}{\|}}{C} - \overset{CH_3}{\underset{H}{\overline{N}}}.$$

Pushing the pi electrons of the carbonyl bond toward the oxygen atom will generate a new resonance structure. Thus,

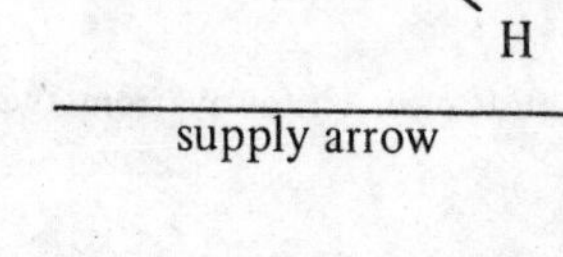

gives

supply arrow

The unshared electrons on the nitrogen atom in the second structure can be pushed to the positively charged carbonyl carbon and

gives

_____   supply arrow

_____.

The resonance method notation for N-methylacetamide is:

⟷   ⟷

_____   _____   _____.

49. Once again the presence of an aromatic ring enhances greatly the opportunities to push electrons and generate new resonance structures. The nitro group in nitrobenzene is a powerful electron attractor. A pair of pi electrons from the ring can be pushed toward the nitrogen atom as the pair of pi electrons in the N-O double bond are pushed toward the oxygen atom. That is,

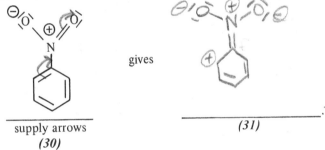

gives

supply arrows
(30)

_____.
(31)

In *31* a pair of pi electrons in the ring can be pushed toward the positive charge. Thus,

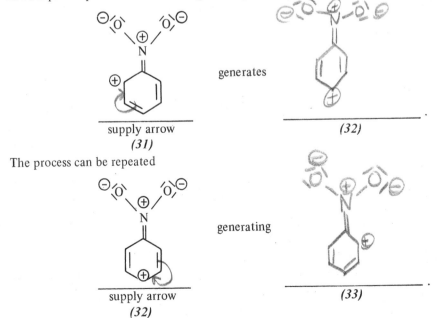

generates

supply arrow
(31)

_____.
(32)

The process can be repeated

generating

supply arrow
(32)

_____.
(33)

The complete resonance method notation for nitrobenzene is: (Watch out for three other structures that can be generated from *30*.)

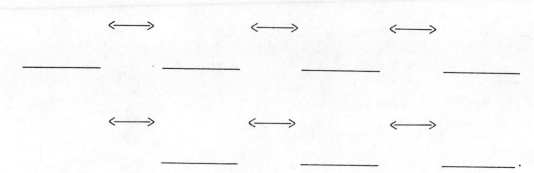

Exercises

One Lewis structure is provided along with the total number of resonance structures (including the one provided). Write the others.

50. Cyclohexen-3-one (3)

51. Ethyl acetate (3)

$$CH_3 — C — \bar{O} — CH_2 — CH_3$$

52. Propionic acid (3)

$$H — \bar{O} — C — CH_2 — CH_3$$

53. Benzonitrile (7)

CHAPTER 2

1. $CH_3-CH=CH-CH_2^{\oplus}$, $CH_3-\overset{\oplus}{C}H-CH=CH_2$

2.

3. pi, oxygen, $CH_3{\diagdown \atop CH_3}C=\overset{\oplus}{O}-H$, $CH_3{\diagdown \atop CH_3}\overset{\oplus}{C}-\bar{O}-H$

4. $\overset{\oplus}{}\,\bar{O}-H$ (above) $CH_3-\overset{\|}{C}-CH_2-CH_3$, $|\bar{O}-H$ (above) $CH_3-\overset{\oplus}{C}-CH_2-CH_3$

5.

6. n (unshared), oxygen, carbon, receptor,

   $CH_3-\bar{O}-\overset{\oplus}{C}H_2$, $CH_3-\overset{\oplus}{O}=CH_2$

7. carbon, $CH_3-C\equiv\overset{\oplus}{O}$

8. $CH_3-\underset{\underset{CH_3}{|}}{C}H-\overset{\oplus}{C}=\bar{O}$, $CH_3-\underset{\underset{CH_3}{|}}{C}H-C=\overset{\oplus}{O}$

9. pushable electrons, receptor

10. $CH_3{\diagdown \atop CH_3}C=CH-\overset{\oplus}{C}H-CH_3 \longleftrightarrow CH_3{\diagdown \atop CH_3}\overset{\oplus}{C}-CH=CH-CH_3$

11. $CH_3{\diagdown \atop CH_3}CH-\underset{\underset{H}{|}}{C}=\overset{\oplus}{\bar{O}}-H \longleftrightarrow CH_3{\diagdown \atop CH_3}CH-\underset{\underset{H}{|}}{\overset{\oplus}{C}}-\bar{O}-H$

12. no additional structures

13.

14. no additional structures

15.

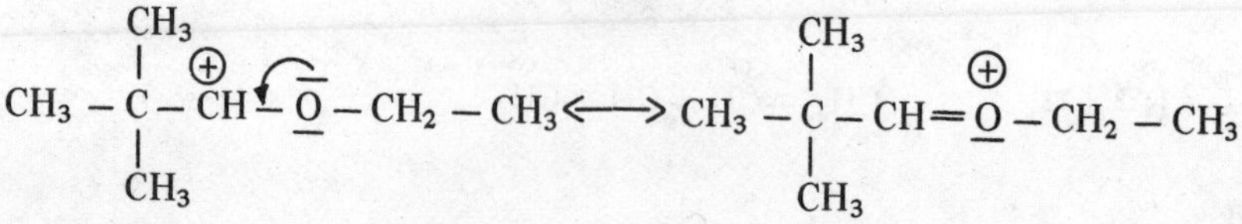

16.

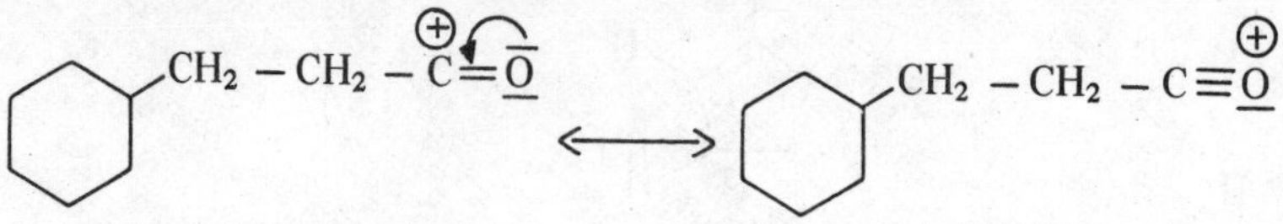

17.

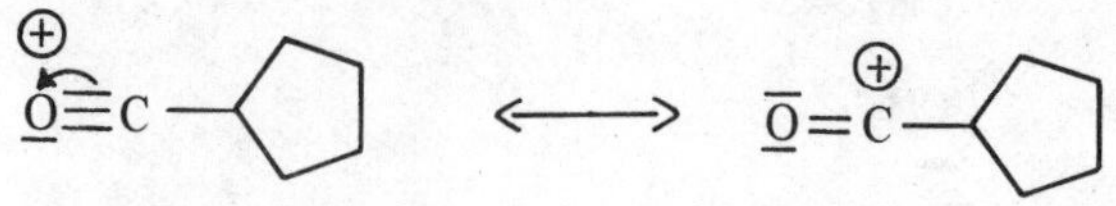

18.

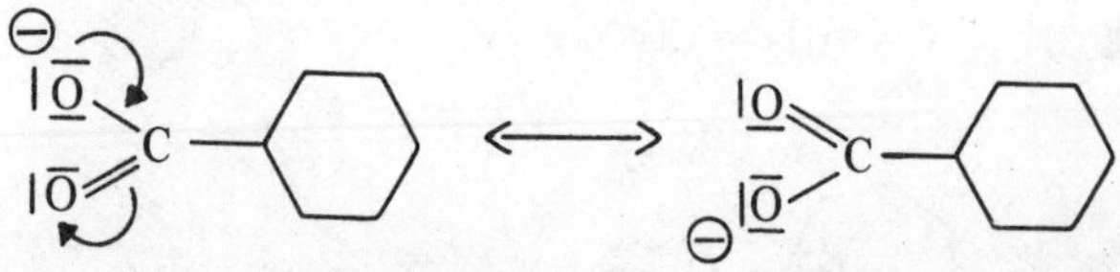

19.

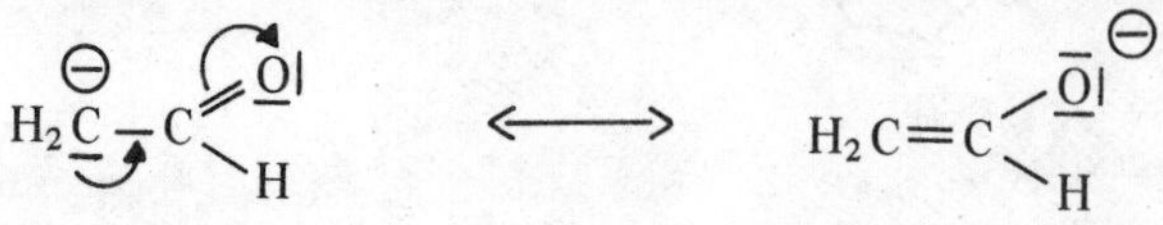

20.

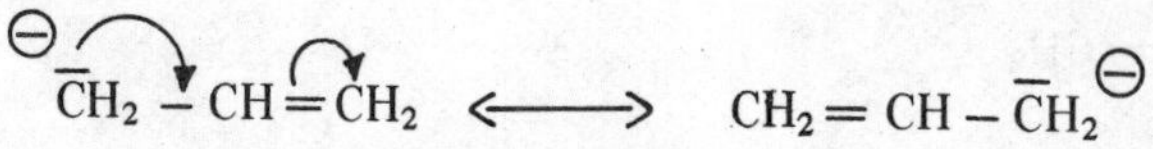

21.

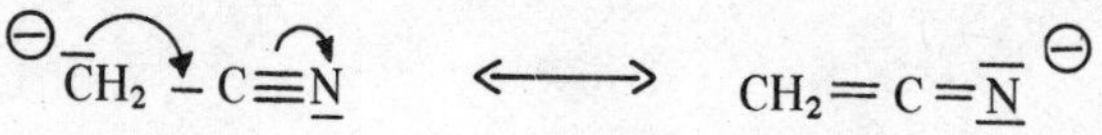

22.

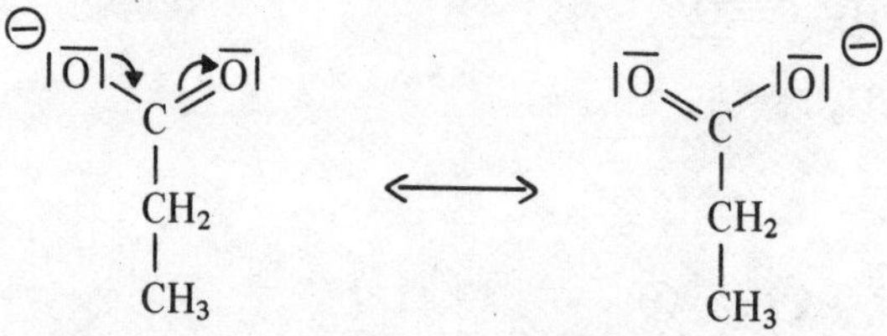

23.

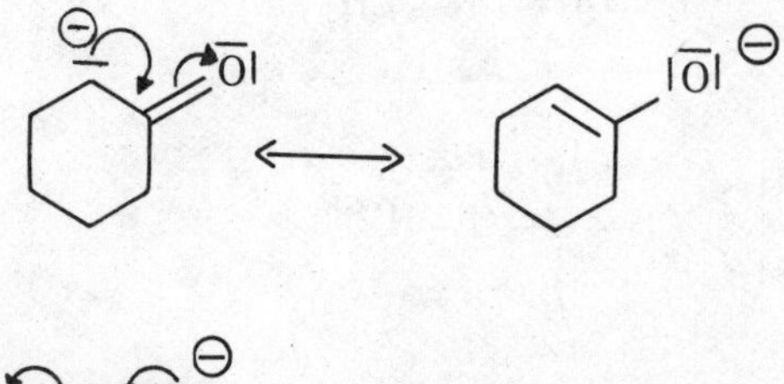

24.

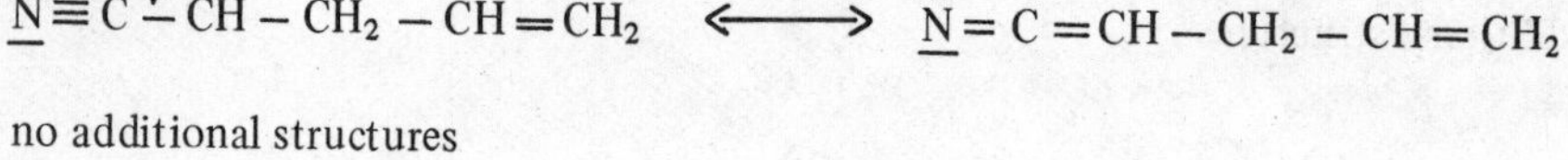

25. no additional structures

26. no additional structures

27.

28. no additional structures

29.

30.

31.

32.

33.

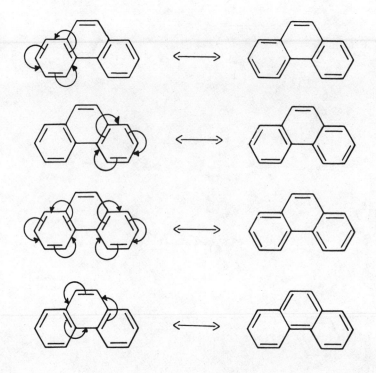

34.

$$CH_2 - CH_3$$

35.

$$CH_3$$

$$CH_3$$

36.

37.

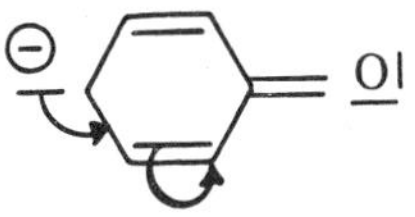

(10) 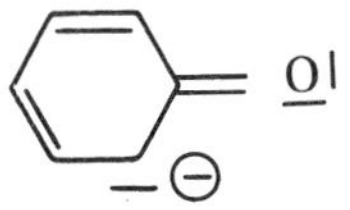 *(11)*

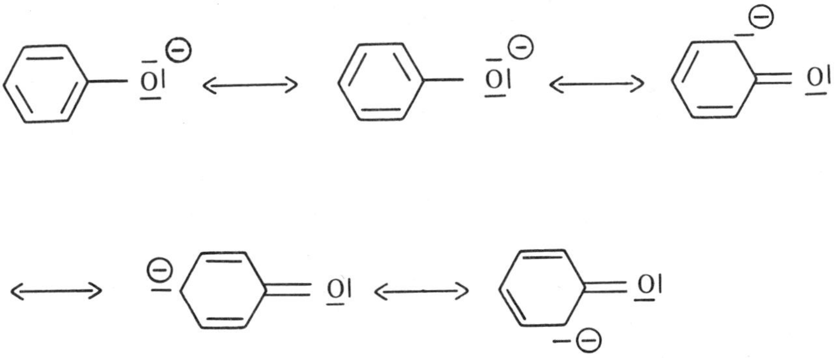

(13) , *(13)* ⟷ *(14)* ,

(14) ⟷ *(15)* , *(15)* ⟷ *(16)*

38.

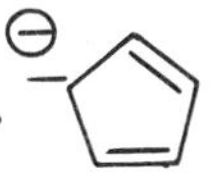

39.

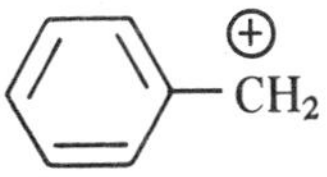

CH_2 *(18)* , $=CH_2$ *(19)* ,

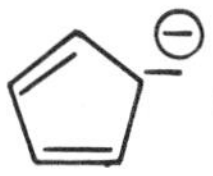

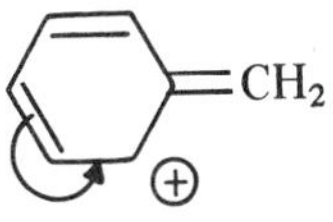

$=CH_2$ *(19)* ⟷ $=CH_2$ *(20)* ,

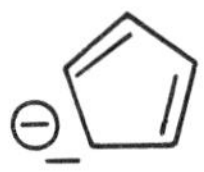

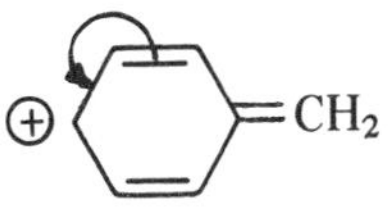

$=CH_2$ *(20)* ⟷ $=CH_2$ *(21)*

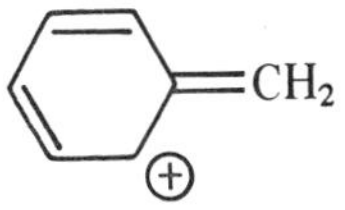

40.

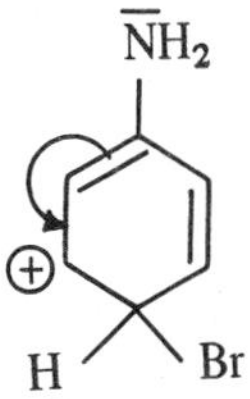

$\overline{N}H_2$ *(22)* 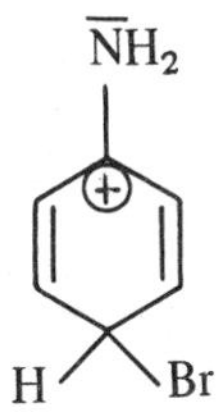 , $\overline{N}H_2$ *(23)* , $\overline{N}H_2$ *(23)* 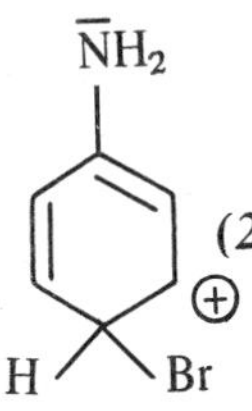 , $\overline{N}H_2$ *(24)* ,

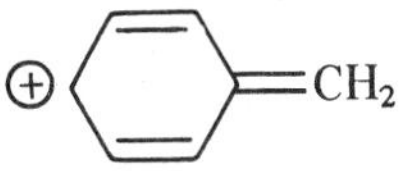

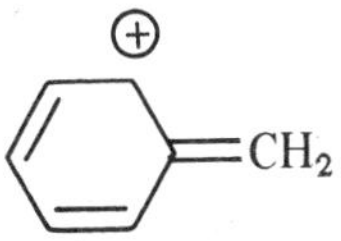

H Br   H Br   H Br   H Br

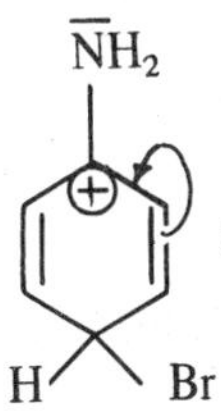

(23)   (25),   structures *22, 23, 24,* and *25*

41.

(26) $\longleftrightarrow$ (27) ,

(27) $\longleftrightarrow$ (28) ,

(27) $\longleftrightarrow$ (29)

42.

$\longleftrightarrow$ $\longleftrightarrow$

43.

$\longleftrightarrow$ $\longleftrightarrow$

A fourth structure,

is not included because the sp-hybridized nitrogen requires that it and the two adjacent carbon atoms be linear. This adds excessive ring strain to the structure.

44.

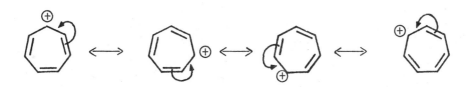

45.

46.

47.

48.

49.

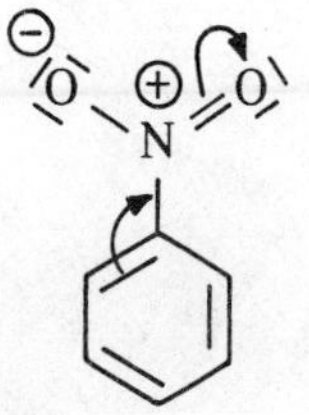

(30)

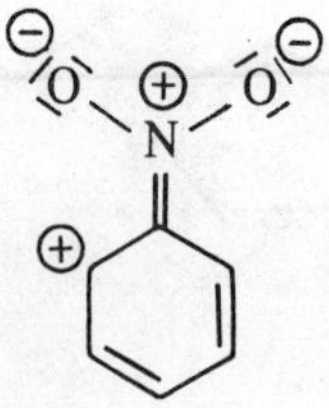

(31) ,

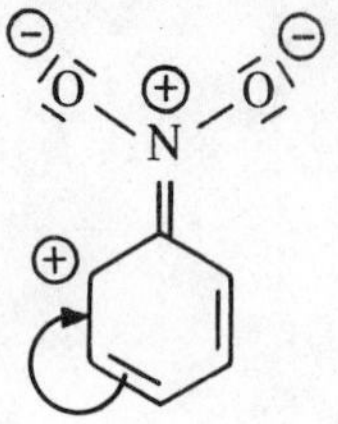

(31)

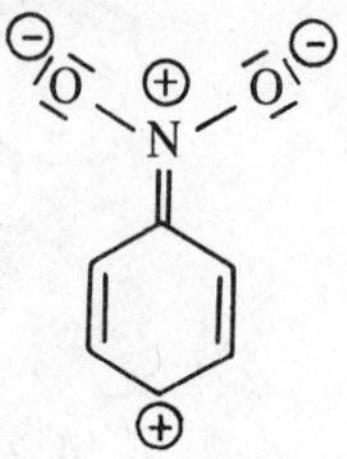

(32) ,

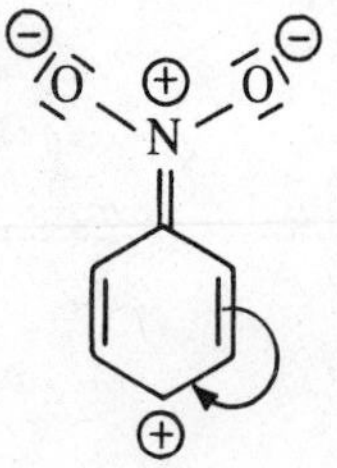

(32)

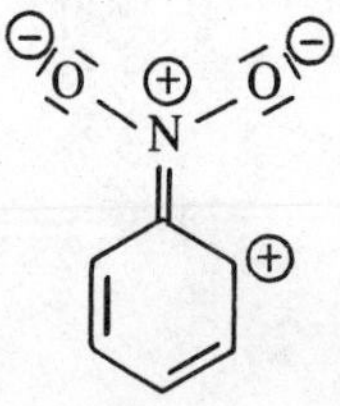

(33) ,

structures *30* through *33* plus:

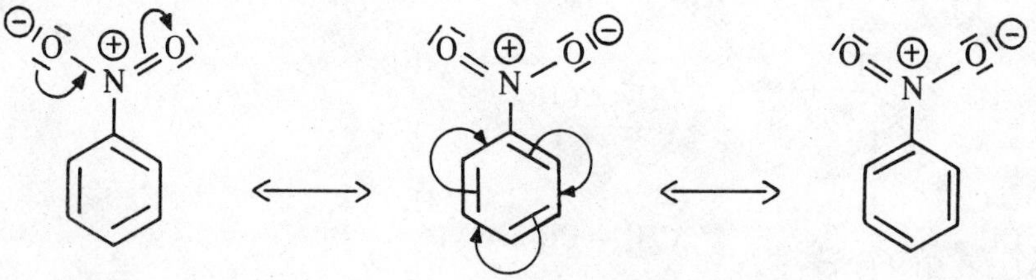

50.

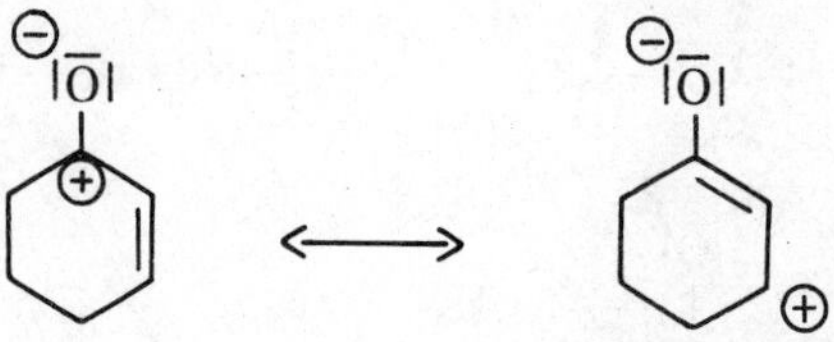

51.

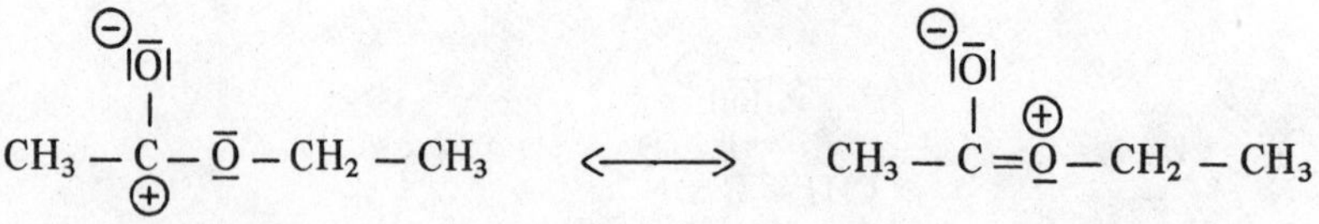

$$CH_3 - \overset{\ominus |\overline{O}|}{\underset{\oplus}{C}} - \overline{O} - CH_2 - CH_3 \quad \longleftrightarrow \quad CH_3 - C = \overset{\oplus}{\underline{O}} - CH_2 - CH_3$$

with $\ominus|\overline{O}|$ above

52.

$$H - \overline{O} - \overset{\ominus |\overline{O}|}{\underset{\oplus}{C}} - CH_2 - CH_3 \quad \longleftrightarrow \quad H - \overset{\oplus}{\underline{O}} = C - CH_2 - CH_3$$

with $\ominus|\overline{O}|$ above

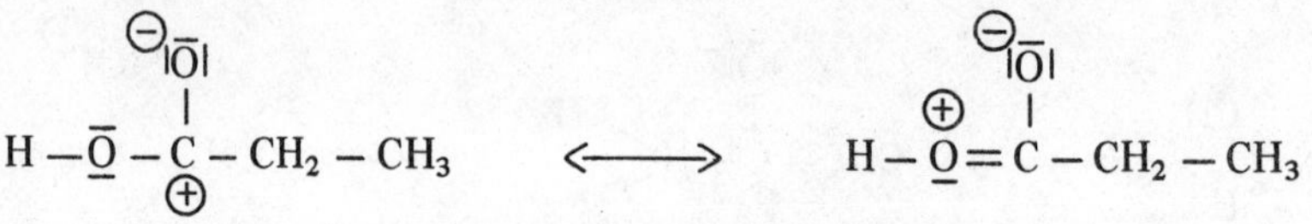

53.

CHAPTER 3

MECHANISMS

In the previous Chapter resonance structures were generated by pushing electrons. Bonds (usually pi bonds) were made and broken. A mechanism consists of a series of steps beginning with starting materials and ending with products. Each step has in it some kind of bond making and/or bond breaking. Sigma bonds as well as pi bonds are involved.

SIGMA BOND BREAKING

Heterolytic cleavage of sigma bonds occurs under a variety of conditions. It is shown as $A \overset{\curvearrowright}{-} B$. The arrow indicates that the sigma electrons which form the A-B bond are leaving A and becoming the exclusive property of B. Since the fragment A is formally losing one electron it must become positively charged and B must become negatively charged since it gains an electron. Thus,

$$A \overset{\curvearrowright}{-} \overline{B}| \longrightarrow A^{\oplus} + |\overline{B}|^{\ominus} .$$

This occurs in the first step of the familiar S_N1 reaction. In t-butyl chloride, the leaving group is chloride ion. The carbon-chlorine bond cleaves, the electrons going with chlorine, which obtains a negative charge. The carbon atom obtains a positive charge. Thus, the cleavage of t-butyl chloride yields chloride ion plus the t-butyl cation.

$$CH_3 - \underset{\underset{CH_3}{|}}{\overset{\overset{CH_3}{|}}{C}} \overset{\curvearrowright}{-} \overline{Cl}| \longrightarrow CH_3 - \underset{\underset{CH_3}{|}}{\overset{\overset{CH_3}{|}}{C}}^{\oplus} \quad |\overline{Cl}|^{\ominus}$$

1. In isopropyl chloride the leaving group is ___Cl⁻___ ion. The ___C___-___Cl___ bond cleaves, the electrons going with ___Cl___, which obtains a

___*neg*___ charge. The carbon atom obtains a ___*pos*___ charge. Thus, the cleavage of isopropyl chloride yields chloride ion plus the ___*isopropyl*___ cation.

$$H-\underset{\underset{CH_3}{|}}{\overset{\overset{CH_3}{|}}{C}}-\underset{\cdot\cdot}{\overline{Cl}}| \longrightarrow \underset{\underset{CH_3}{|}}{\overset{\overset{CH_3}{|}}{H-C\oplus}} \qquad |\overline{\underset{\cdot\cdot}{Cl}}|^{\ominus}$$

2. In cyclohexyl bromide the leaving group is ___*Br⁻*___ ion. The ___*C*___-___*Br*___ bond cleaves, the electrons going with ___*Br*___, which obtains a ___*neg*___ charge. The carbon atom obtains a ___*pos*___ charge. Thus, the cleavage of cyclohexyl bromide yields ___*Br⁻*___ ion plus the ___*cyclohexyl*___ cation.

_____
supply arrow

* * * * *

Very often, heterolytic cleavage occurs from a charged intermediate which was formed in a previous step. The process is the same but the charge on the products is different. Thus,

$$A-\underset{\cdot\cdot}{\overline{B}}-H \longrightarrow A^{\oplus} + |\overline{\underset{\cdot\cdot}{B}}-H$$

3. This kind of cleavage occurs in the second step of the dehydration of alcohols. In the first step the alcohol is protonated to form *1*. In *1*, the leaving group is a <u>water</u> molecule. The <u>carbon-oxygen</u> bond cleaves, the electrons going with the oxygen atom. The <u>oxygen</u> atom, which had a <u>positive</u> charge becomes <u>neutral</u>. The carbon atom obtains a <u>positive</u> charge. Thus, the cleavage of *1* yields <u>water</u> plus the <u>t-butyl</u> cation.

_____
supply arrow
1

4. The acid-catalyzed hydrolysis of methoxymethyl acetate begins with protonation giving *2*. The

$$-CH_2-\underset{\underset{H}{|}}{\overset{\oplus}{\overline{O}}}-$$

bond cleaves, the electrons going with the ___*O*___ atom. The oxygen atom which had a positive charge becomes ___*neutral*___. The leaving group is <u>acetic acid</u>. The carbon atom from which acetic acid departed obtains a ___*pos*___ charge. Thus, the cleavage of *2* yields acetic acid plus the <u>methoxymethyl</u> cation.

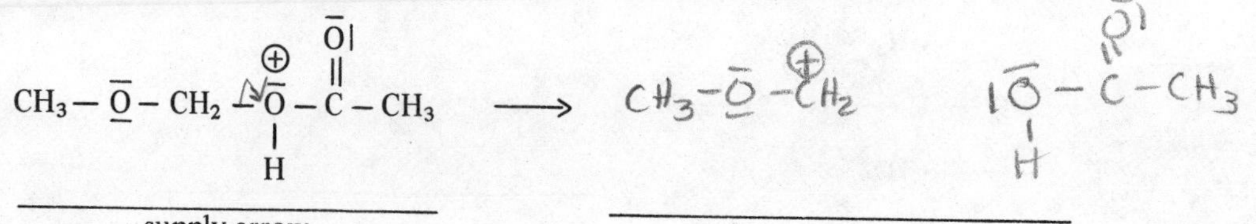

$$CH_3 - \bar{O} - CH_2 \overset{\oplus}{N}O - \overset{\overset{\bar{O}|}{\|}}{C} - CH_3 \longrightarrow CH_3 - \bar{O} - \overset{\oplus}{C}H_2 \qquad |\bar{O} - \overset{\overset{\bar{\overset{..}{O}|}}{}}{\underset{H}{C}} - CH_3$$

_____   _____
supply arrow
2

5. Sometimes a ring will be opened as a result of sigma bond breaking. The protonated epoxide, *3*, will suffer heterolytic cleavage of one of its carbon-oxygen bonds, with the electrons going to the ___*O*___ atom. The oxygen atom, which had a ___*pos*___ charge, becomes ___*neutral*___. The leaving group is

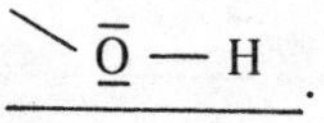

$$\diagdown \bar{O} - H$$
_____

The carbon atom from which the oxygen departed obtains a ___*pos*___ charge. Thus,

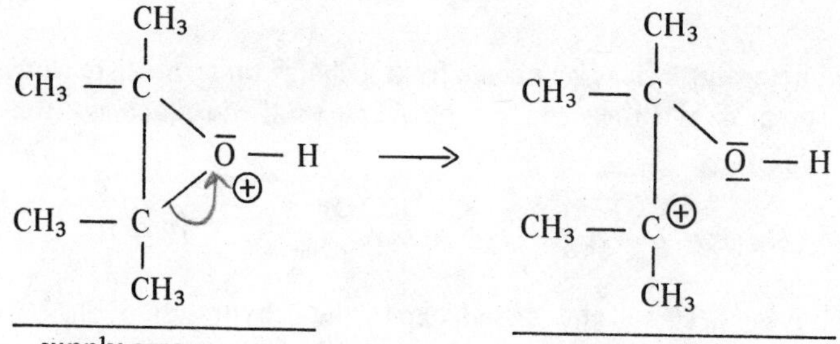

_____   _____
supply arrow
3

Exercises

Here are some exercises in sigma bond breaking. Supply the arrows and the products. Remember that charge must be conserved. That is, if a neutral molecule is dissociated the algebraic sum of the charges on the products must equal zero. If a positively charged ion is dissociated, the algebraic sum of the charges on the products must equal +1.

6.

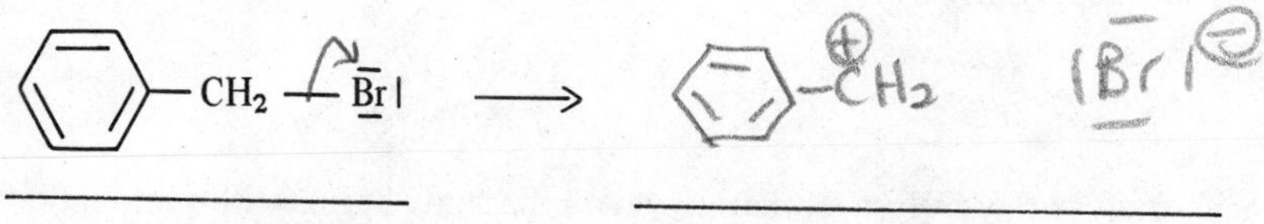

_____   _____

7.

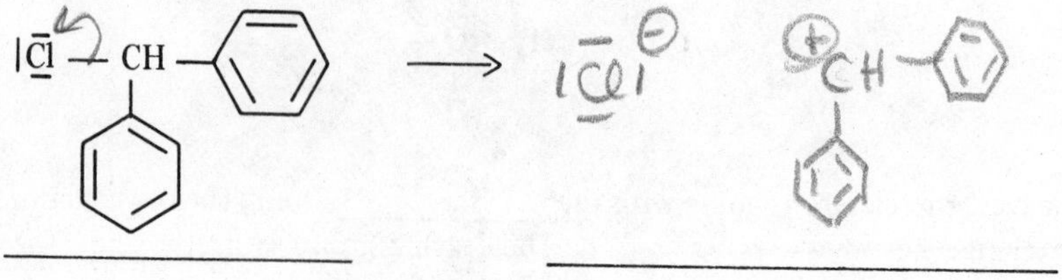

_____   _____

8.

9.

10.

11.

12.

13.

14.

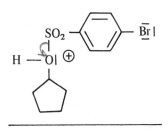

SIGMA BOND MAKING

Formation of a sigma bond occurs when an anion and a cation encounter one another. That is:

$$A^{\oplus} \quad \overline{|\underline{B}|}^{\ominus} \quad \longrightarrow \quad A - \underline{B}| \quad .$$

The arrow indicates that a pair of electrons which was the exclusive property of B is now shared by A and B.

The product forming step in many S_N1 reactions involves the formation of a sigma bond between the intermediate carbocation and some negatively charged nucleophile. For example, α-phenylethyl cation will yield an ester by reaction with acetate ion. A pair of n electrons on the negatively charged <u>oxygen</u> atom forms a bond between <u>oxygen</u> and <u>carbon</u> and becomes a pair of sigma electrons. The oxygen atom which had a <u>negative</u> charge becomes <u>neutral</u> and the carbon atom which had a <u>positive</u> charge becomes <u>neutral</u>.

15. *Sec*-butyl cation will react with bromide ion to form *sec*-butyl bromide. A pair of ___n___ electrons on the negatively charged ___Br⁻___ ion forms a bond between ___Br___ and ___C___ and becomes a pair of ___σ___ electrons. The bromine atom which had a ___neg___ charge becomes ___neutral___ and the carbon atom which had a ___pos___ charge becomes ___neutral___.

$$CH_3 - CH_2 - \underset{\underset{H}{|}}{\overset{\overset{CH_3}{|}}{C}}{}^{\oplus} \quad |\underline{Br}|^{\ominus} \quad \longrightarrow \quad CH_3 - CH_2 - \underset{\underset{H}{|}}{\overset{\overset{CH_3}{|}}{C}} - Br$$

supply arrow

* * * * *

More commonly, sigma bonds are formed by the reaction of carbocations with neutral molecules possessing unshared pairs. The result is a positively charged intermediate.

$$-\overset{|}{\underset{|}{C}}{}^{\oplus} \quad \overset{..}{Nu} \quad \longrightarrow \quad -\overset{|}{\underset{|}{C}} - \overset{\oplus}{Nu}$$

16. In the <u>solvolysis</u> of alkyl halides in ethanol, a carbocation resulting from heterolytic cleavage forms a sigma bond with one of the unshared pairs on the alcohol oxygen atom. A pair of <u>n</u> electrons on the oxygen atom forms a bond between <u>oxygen</u> and <u>carbon</u> and becomes a pair of

sigma electrons. The oxygen atom, which was <u>neutral</u>, now possesses a formal <u>positive</u> charge. The carbon atom, which had a <u>positive</u> charge, is now <u>neutral</u>.

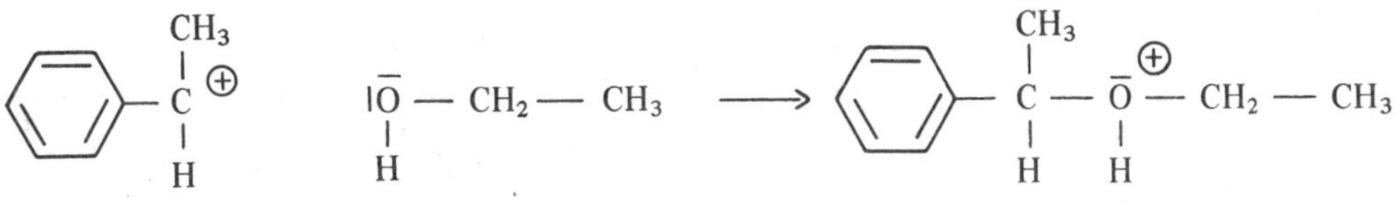

supply arrow

17. Carbocations will react with amines in an analogous process. The __n__ electrons on the nitrogen atom form a bond between __N__ and __C__ and becomes a pair of __σ__ electrons. The nitrogen atom, which was neutral, now possesses a formal __pos__ charge. The carbon atom which had a __pos__ charge is now __neutral__.

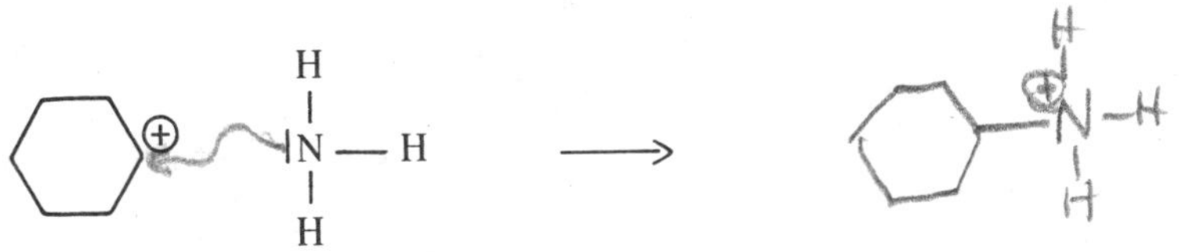

supply arrow

*   *   *   *   *

Some important features of the way electron pushing is used to write mechanisms should be noted:

(a) Electrons are always pushed *toward* a center of positive charge.

(b) Although the position of positive charge changes, the positive charge is *not* pushed. Arrows should never lead away from a positive charge.

(c) Total charge is conserved. That is, the sum of the charges on one side of the equation always equal the sum of the charges on the other.

(d) Electrons are conserved. That is, the number of valence electrons on each side of an equation is always equal.

Exercises

Here are some examples of sigma bond making. Supply the arrows and the products.

18.

19.

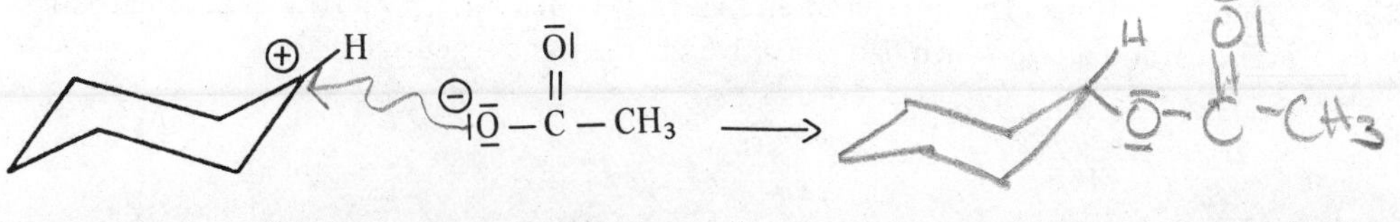

_____   _____

20.

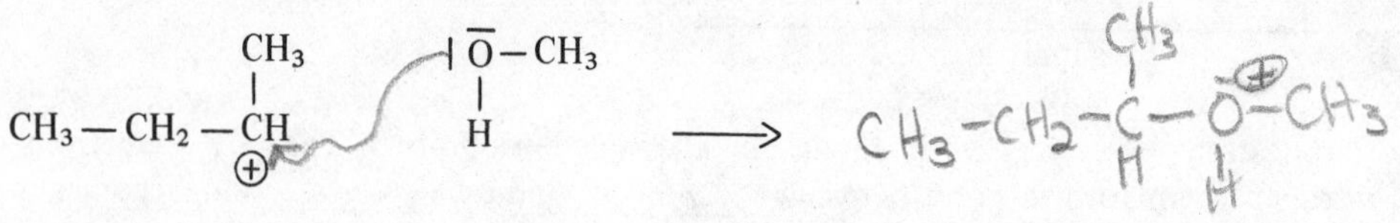

_____   _____

21.

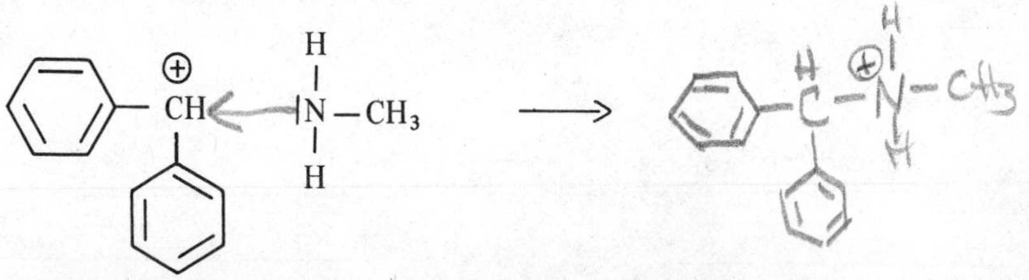

_____   _____

22.

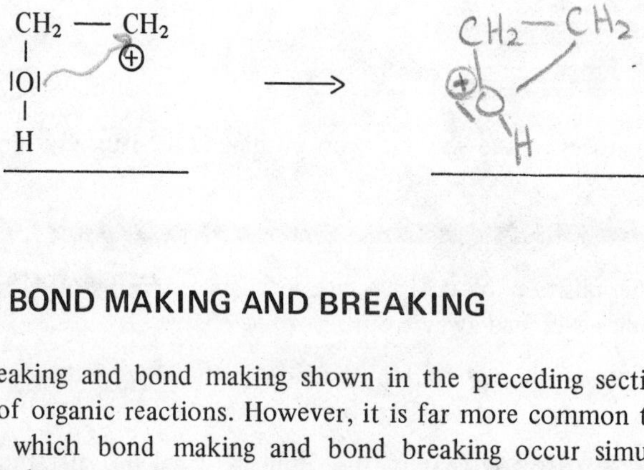

_____   _____

SIMULTANEOUS BOND MAKING AND BREAKING

Isolated bond breaking and bond making shown in the preceding sections are important in writing mechanisms of organic reactions. However, it is far more common to encounter steps in organic reactions in which bond making and bond breaking occur simultaneously. In some instances bond making has proceeded well along toward completion and bond breaking has only begun as the transition state is reached. The opposite can also occur. However, these are fine points of mechanism and need not concern a student just learning to push electrons.

SIGMA BOND MAKING – SIGMA BOND BREAKING

The simultaneous making and breaking of sigma bonds is illustrated nicely in the familiar S_N2 reaction. A negatively charged nucleophile, $\overline{Nu}^{\ominus}$ approaches a carbon atom having a leaving group, $-L$, in a direction anti to and rearward to the leaving group. The pushable electrons are possessed by the nucleophile and the receptor is the carbon atom which itself has a pair of pushable electrons, namely, the sigma electrons forming the C–L bond. The products are a compound having a C–Nu bond and the anion of the leaving group. Thus, Nu has been substituted for L.

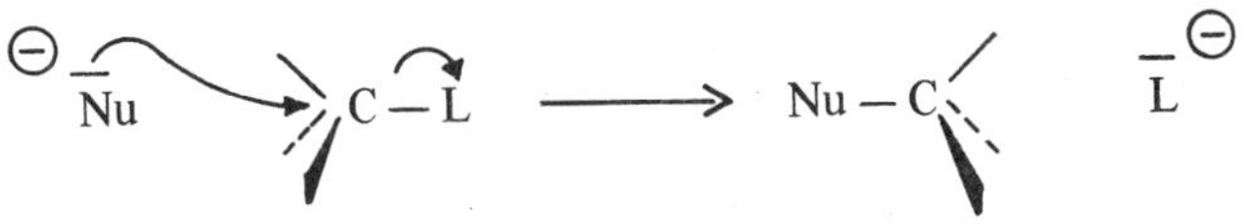

(See footnote 1.)

The S_N2 reaction of methyl iodide with chloride ion illustrates this process. The nucleophile is chloride ion. The leaving group is iodide ion. A pair of n electrons on the chloride ion is pushed toward the carbon atom and, simultaneously, the sigma electrons of the carbon-iodine bond are pushed toward iodine. The result is the making of a sigma bond between chlorine and carbon, and the breaking of a sigma bond between carbon and iodine. The chlorine, which had a negative charge, becomes neutral and the iodine, which was neutral, now possesses a formal negative charge.

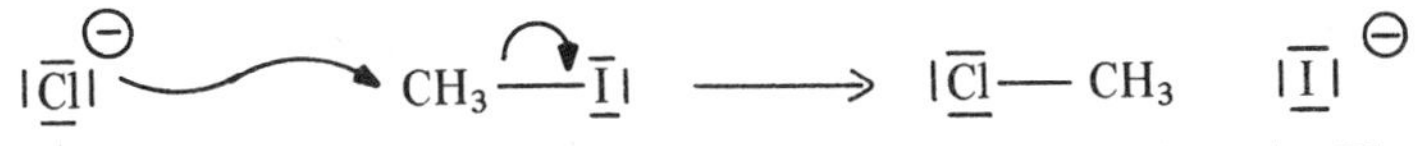

23. Another example is the reaction of hydroxide ion with ethyl chloride. The nucleophile is OH^- ion. The leaving group is Cl^- ion. A pair of n electrons from hydroxide ion is pushed toward the carbon atom and, simultaneously, the σ electrons of the carbon-chlorine bond are pushed toward Cl. The result is the making of a sigma bond between oxygen and C and the breaking of the sigma bond between carbon and Cl. The oxygen, which had a negative charge, is now neutral and the chlorine, which was neutral, now possesses a formal neg charge.

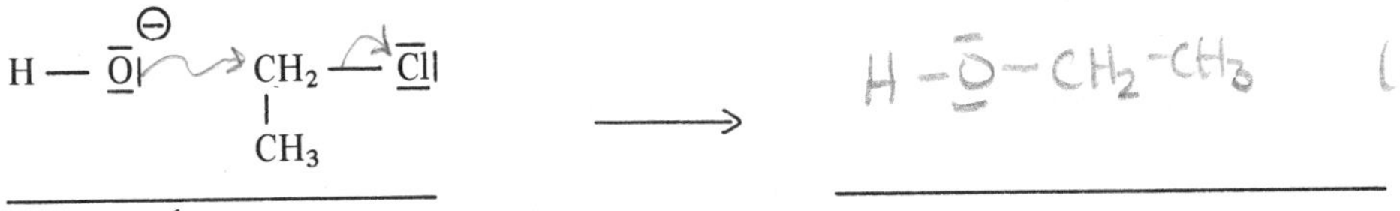

supply arrows

24. Another example is the reaction of hydroxide ion with benzyl bromide.

supply arrows

* * * * *

[1] This illustrative equation has been written in the stereochemically accurate form showing that an inversion of configuration occurs during S_N2 reactions. It was done this way to make the illustration as clear as possible. However, the student should note that the S_N2 reaction is usually written without reference to stereochemistry unless a stereochemical point is being made. Thus, the reaction is usually written:

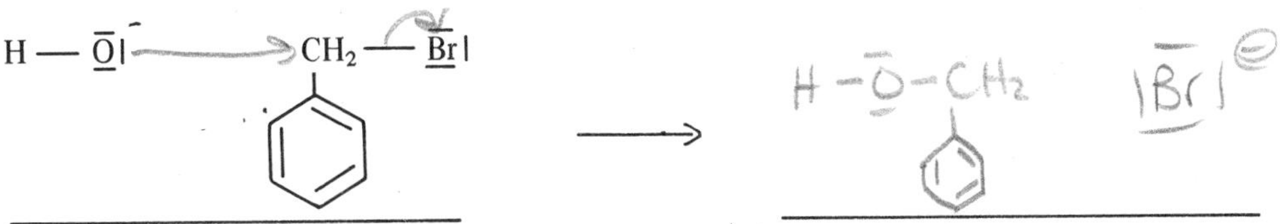

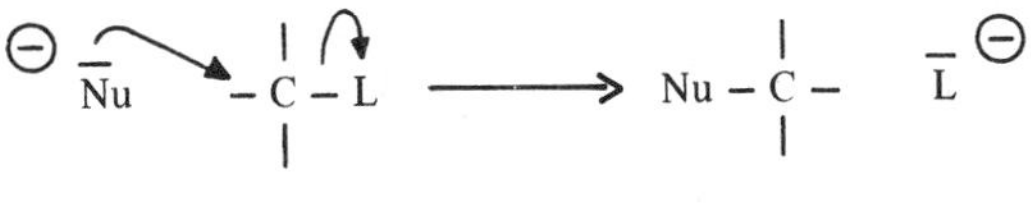

Carbon need not always be the center of this type of reaction. For example, the removal of an acidic proton from an organic compound by a base is a common occurrence.

25. The reaction of phenol with hydroxide ion results in the phenoxide ion plus a molecule of water. A pair of n electrons on the oxygen atom of the hydroxide ion is pushed toward the hydrogen atom and, simultaneously, the sigma electrons of the bond between the hydrogen and oxygen atoms of phenol are pushed toward oxygen. The result is the making of a sigma bond between oxygen and _____H_____ and the breaking of a sigma bond between hydrogen and _____O_____ . The oxygen atom of the former hydroxide ion, which had a negative charge, is now neutral and the oxygen atom of phenol, which was neutral now possesses a formal negative charge.

26. The amide ion is a strong enough base to remove a proton from acetylene. The reaction results in a molecule of ammonia plus the acetylide anion. A pair of _n_ electrons on the _____N_____ atom of the amide ion is pushed toward the hydrogen atom and, simultaneously, the _____σ_____ electrons of the carbon-hydrogen bond of acetylene are pushed toward _____C_____ . Thus, a sigma bond is made between nitrogen and _____H_____ , and a sigma bond is broken between hydrogen and _____C_____ . The nitrogen atom which possessed a negative charge in the amide ion is now _neutral_ and the carbon atom which was neutral in acetylene now possesses a _neg_ charge.

supply arrows

27. The reaction of ethoxide ion with one of the alpha hydrogens of acetaldehyde is another example. The products are a molecule of ethanol and the anion of acetaldehyde.

supply arrows

*   *   *   *   *

The formation of a carbon-carbon sigma bond occurs in the reaction of a Grignard reagent with ethylene oxide. In the illustration the Grignard reagent, ethyl magnesium bromide, is written as an ion pair consisting of the MgBr⊕ ion and the ethyl anion. The nucleophile is the ethyl anion. A pair of n electrons on the carbanion is pushed toward one of the carbon atoms of ethylene oxide. Simultaneously, the sigma electrons of the carbon-oxygen bond are pushed toward oxygen. The result is a ring-opening. The carbanion, which had a negative charge, has become neutral and the oxygen atom of ethylene oxide, which was neutral, now possesses a formal negative charge.

28. In the reaction of n-propyl magnesium iodide with ethylene oxide the nucleophile is the ___propyl___ anion. A pair of ___∩___ electrons on the carbanion is pushed toward one of the ___C___ atoms of ethylene oxide. Simultaneously, the ___σ___ electrons of the carbon-___O___ bond are pushed toward ___O___. Thus, a sigma bond has been made between carbon and___C___, and a sigma bond has been broken between carbon and ___O___. The carbanion, which had a negative charge, has become ___neutral___ and the oxygen atom of ethylene oxide, which was neutral, now possesses a ___neg___ charge.

supply arrows

29. Analogously, an alcoholate anion will open an epoxide ring. In the reaction of ethoxide ion with 2-butene oxide the nucleophile is ___oxide___ ion. A pair of ___∩___ electrons on the ___O___ atom of the ethoxide ion is pushed toward one of the___C___ atoms in 2-butene oxide. Simultaneously, the ___σ___ electrons of the carbon-___O___ bond are pushed toward___O___. Thus, a sigma bond has been made between oxygen and___C___, and a sigma bond has been broken between carbon and ___O___. The ethoxide ion, which had a negative charge, has become ___neutral___ and the oxygen atom of 2-butene oxide, which was neutral, now possesses a ___neg___ charge.

supply arrows

*   *   *   *   *

The simultaneous making and breaking of sigma bonds occurs also between a neutral nucleophile or base with pushable electrons and a positively charged species which can act as a receptor.

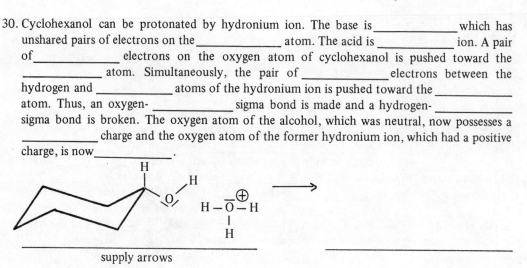

In organic chemistry the most common examples of this are reactions in which a molecule possessing unshared electrons is protonated by a positively charged acid.

Alcohols are protonated by hydronium ion ($H_3O^{\oplus}$). In the reaction of *t*-butyl alcohol with hydronium ion the base is *t*-butyl alcohol which has unshared pairs on the oxygen atom. The acid is hydronium ion. The n electrons on the oxygen atom of *t*-butyl alcohol are pushed toward the hydrogen atom. Simultaneously, the pair of sigma electrons between the hydrogen and oxygen atoms of the hydronium ion is pushed toward the oxygen atom. Thus, an oxygen-hydrogen sigma bond is made and a hydrogen-oxygen sigma bond is broken. The oxygen atom of the alcohol, which was neutral, now possesses a formal positive charge and the oxygen atom of the hydronium ion, which had a positive charge, is now neutral.

30. Cyclohexanol can be protonated by hydronium ion. The base is _____ which has unshared pairs of electrons on the _____ atom. The acid is _____ ion. A pair of _____ electrons on the oxygen atom of cyclohexanol is pushed toward the _____ atom. Simultaneously, the pair of _____ electrons between the hydrogen and _____ atoms of the hydronium ion is pushed toward the _____ atom. Thus, an oxygen- _____ sigma bond is made and a hydrogen- _____ sigma bond is broken. The oxygen atom of the alcohol, which was neutral, now possesses a _____ charge and the oxygen atom of the former hydronium ion, which had a positive charge, is now _____ .

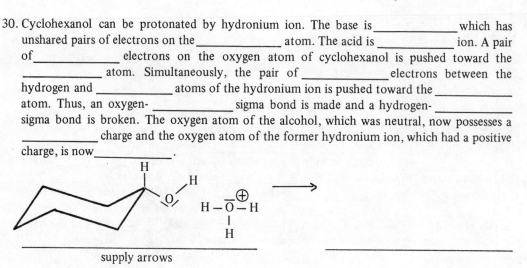

supply arrows

31. The reaction just described is reversible. Deprotonation of the conjugate acid of an organic base by water provides another example of simultaneous making and breaking of sigma bonds. Thus, in the deprotonation of anilinium ion by water, the base is water which has unshared electrons on the _____ atom. The acid is _____ ion. A pair of _____ electrons on the oxygen atom of water is pushed toward the _____ atom. Simultaneously, the pair of _____ electrons between the hydrogen and _____ atoms of the anilinium ion is pushed toward the _____ atom. Thus, an oxygen- _____ sigma bond is made and a hydrogen- _____ sigma bond is broken. The nitrogen atom, which possessed a positive charge, is now _____ and the oxygen atom, which was neutral, now possesses a formal _____ charge.

supply arrows

32. Let us consider an entire mechanism of an organic reaction. The acid-catalyzed ring-opening of epoxides is initiated by protonation on the epoxide oxygen by hydronium ion.

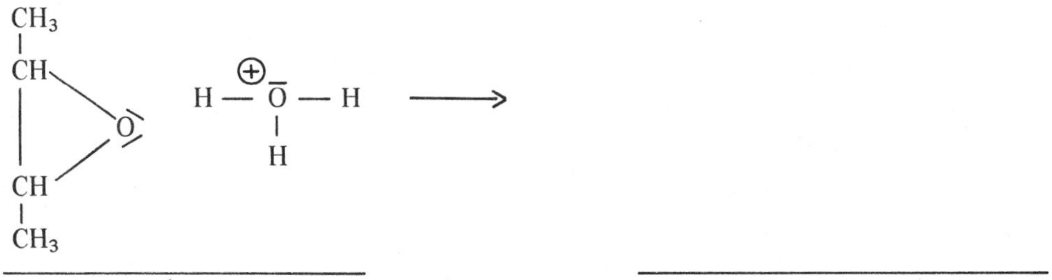

supply arrows

33. The resulting ion then suffers nucleophilic attack on carbon by the neutral molecule, water, and the ring is opened.

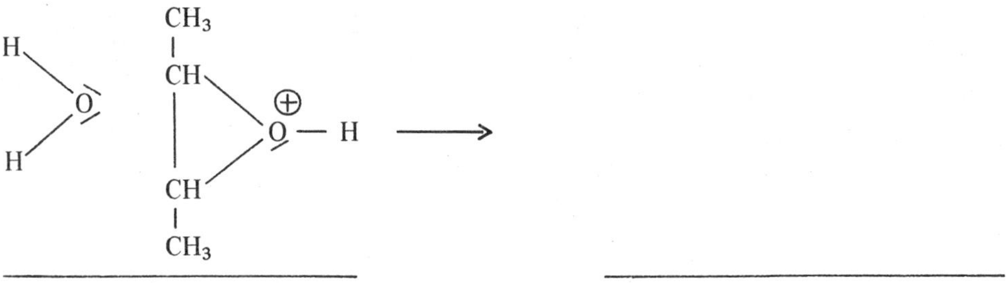

supply arrows

34. The resulting ion is then deprotonated by water giving a hydronium ion plus the organic product, a neutral 1,2-diol.

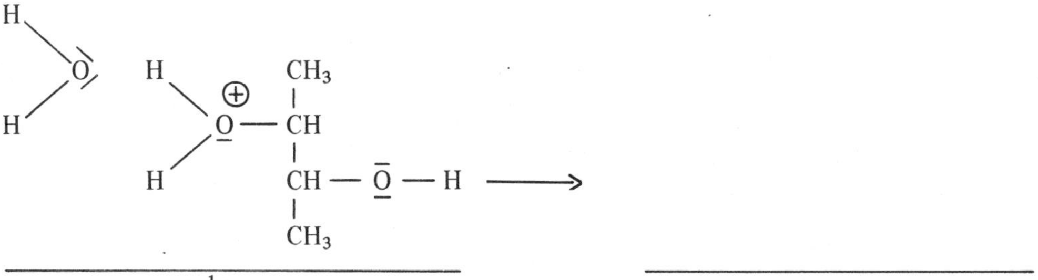

supply arrows

Thus, all three steps in this organic reaction are examples of simultaneous sigma bond making–sigma bond breaking.

Exercises

Here are some examples of simultaneous sigma bond making and sigma bond breaking. Where arrows are supplied, write in the products. Where the products are written in, supply the appropriate arrows.

35.

36.

$$CH_3 - CH_2 - \overset{\oplus}{\underset{|}{\overline{O}}} - H \quad \overset{H}{\underset{|}{|\overline{O}}} - H \quad \longrightarrow \quad CH_3 - CH_2 - \overline{O}| \quad \overset{\oplus}{\underset{|}{H}} - \overset{}{\overline{O}} - H$$

37.

$$\bigcirc - \overset{\ominus}{\overline{O}|} \curvearrowright \overset{CH_3}{\underset{}{CH_2}} \curvearrowleft \overline{I}| \quad \longrightarrow$$

38. $$CH_3 - CH_2 - \overline{O} \diagdown C = \overline{O} \quad H - \overline{O} - SO_3H \longrightarrow \quad CH_3 - CH_2 - \overline{O} \diagdown \overset{\oplus}{C} = \overset{}{\underset{|}{\overline{O}}} - H \quad \overset{\ominus}{|\overline{O}} - SO_3H$$
$$\underset{CH_3}{} \qquad\qquad\qquad\qquad\qquad \underset{CH_3}{}$$

39.

$$\overset{H}{\underset{\bigcirc}{C}} = \overset{\oplus}{\overline{O}} - H \longleftarrow \overset{\ominus}{|\overline{O}} - \overset{\overset{\overline{O}|}{||}}{C} - CH_3 \quad \longrightarrow$$

40.

$$\overset{H_3C}{\underset{H_3C}{}} \overset{\ominus}{\underset{\oplus}{\overline{C}H}} \quad \overset{CH_3}{\underset{CH_3}{\overset{|}{CH} \diagup \overset{}{\underset{CH}{|}} \diagdown O}} \longrightarrow \quad \overset{CH_3 \quad CH_3}{CH_3 - CH - CH} \quad \overset{\oplus}{MgBr}$$

$$\underset{MgBr}{} \qquad\qquad\qquad \overset{|}{\underset{CH_3}{CH - \overset{\ominus}{\overline{O}|}}}$$

41. $$CH_3 - CH_2 \diagdown \overset{H}{\underset{}{N}} \longrightarrow H \overset{}{\underset{}{\overline{O}}} - \overset{\overset{\overline{O}|}{||}}{C} - CH_3 \longrightarrow$$
$$CH_3 - CH_2 \diagup$$

42. $$\overset{CH_3}{\underset{CH_3}{CH_3 - \overset{|}{C} - \overset{\ominus}{\overline{O}|}}} \quad CH_3 - \overline{Br}| \longrightarrow \quad \overset{CH_3}{\underset{CH_3}{CH_3 - \overset{|}{C} - \overline{O} - CH_3}} \quad \overset{\ominus}{|\overline{Br}|}$$

SIGMA BOND MAKING – PI BOND BREAKING

There are many steps in organic reactions in which a sigma bond is formed at the same time that a pi bond is broken. In each case, this results in a condensation of a molecule and an ion into a single ion. Actually, this category of reactions can be divided according to whether the electrons being pushed are n electrons or pi electrons.

A negatively charged nucleophile may react with a pi bond as follows:

$$\overset{\ominus}{\underline{Nu}} \quad \overset{\frown}{C = X} \quad \longrightarrow \quad Nu - \overset{|}{\underset{|}{C}} - \overset{\ominus}{\overline{X}}$$

In this case, the electrons being pushed are the n electrons on the nucleophile. The receptor is the carbon atom in the double bond which has a pair of pushable electrons itself. Pushing the n electrons to the carbon atom results in the Nu—C sigma bond. Pushing the pi electrons away from the carbon atom breaks the pi bond and places a formal negative charge on the atom X. Overall, the single negative charge has been conserved.

43. The first step in the saponification of ethyl acetate involves a reaction in which hydroxide ion attacks the carbonyl-carbon atom. The nucleophile is a _____ ion. A pair of _____ electrons on the oxygen atom of hydroxide ion is pushed toward the carbonyl-carbon atom. The pair of pi electrons of the carbon-oxygen double bond of ethyl acetate is pushed toward the _____ atom. A sigma bond has been made between oxygen and carbon. A pi bond has been broken between carbon and _____ . The hydroxyl oxygen, which had a negative charge, is now neutral and the carbonyl oxygen, which was neutral, now possesses a _____ charge.

$$CH_3 - \overset{\overline{O}|}{\underset{\underset{H}{\ominus|\underline{O}-H}}{\overset{\|}{C}}} - \underline{O} - CH_2 - CH_3 \quad \longrightarrow \quad CH_3 - \overset{|\overline{O}|\overset{\ominus}{}}{\underset{|O-H}{\overset{|}{C}}} - \underline{O} - CH_2 - CH_3$$

44. Similarly, amides are attacked by hydroxide ion. The nucleophile is _____ ion. A pair of _____ electrons on the hydroxyl oxygen atom is pushed toward the carbonyl-carbon atom. The pair of _____ electrons in the carbon- _____ double bond is pushed toward the _____ atom. A sigma bond has been made between oxygen and _____ . A pi bond has been broken between carbon and _____ . The hydroxyl oxygen, which had a negative charge, is now _____ . The carbonyl oxygen, which was neutral, now possesses a _____ charge.

$$\bigcirc - \overset{\overline{O}|}{\underset{\underset{}{\ominus|\underline{O}-H}}{\overset{\|}{C}}} - \overline{N}H - CH_3 \quad \longrightarrow$$

_____   _____
supply arrows

45. The first step in the formation of a cyanohydrin under neutral or basic conditions involves a similar process.

$$N \equiv \overset{\ominus}{\underline{C}} \qquad \overset{R}{\underset{R}{\diagdown}} C = \underline{O}| \quad \longrightarrow$$

_____   _____
supply arrows

46. Since the alkyl portion of a Grignard reagent can be treated as a carbanion, its well known reaction with a carbonyl group fits this category.

$$CH_3 - CH_2 - \overset{\ominus}{\overline{C}H_2} \qquad \overset{H}{\underset{\begin{array}{c} | \\ CH_2 \\ | \\ CH \\ \diagup \quad \diagdown \\ CH_3 \qquad CH_3 \end{array}}{\overset{|}{C}} = \underline{O}| \qquad \longrightarrow$$

$$\overset{\oplus}{MgBr}$$

————————————————   ————————————————
                 supply arrows

47. The pi bond which is broken can be part of a triple bond. Consider the first step in the base-catalyzed hydrolysis of a nitrile.

(benzene ring)$- C \equiv \underline{N}$

$$\longrightarrow$$

$$\overset{\ominus}{|\underline{O}} - H$$

————————————————   ————————————————
          supply arrows

*   *   *.   *   *

A slight variation of this process occurs when the nucleophile possessing the pushable n electrons is neutral. In virtually all of these cases, the pi system must have suffered some kind of previous activation in order for the reaction to proceed at a reasonable rate. The activation process (usually protonation) puts a positive charge on the pi system. Thus,

$$\overline{Nu} \qquad C = \overset{\oplus}{X} \qquad \longrightarrow \qquad \overset{\oplus}{Nu} - \overset{|}{\underset{|}{C}} - \overline{X}$$

48. We have already seen that hydroxide ion, a strong nucleophile, will attack the carbonyl-carbon atom of an ester. Analogously, water, a weak nucleophile, will attack the carbonyl-carbon atom of a protonated ester. A pair of n electrons on the oxygen atom of the water molecule is pushed toward the carbonyl-carbon atom. The pair of pi electrons of the carbon-oxygen double bond is pushed toward the oxygen atom. Thus, a sigma bond has been made between oxygen and _____ , and a pi bond has been broken between carbon and _____ . The oxygen atom of the water molecule, which was neutral, now possesses a _____ charge. The carbonyl-oxygen atom, which had a positive charge, is now _____ .

$$CH_3 - \overset{\overset{\displaystyle \oplus}{\overset{\displaystyle O|}{\|}}}{C} - \underline{O} - CH_2 - CH_3 \qquad \longrightarrow \qquad CH_3 - \overset{\overset{\displaystyle |O|}{|}}{\underset{\underset{\underset{H}{|}}{\overset{\oplus}{|O} - H}}{C}} - \underline{O} - CH_2 - CH_3$$

$$\underset{\underset{H}{|}}{|\underline{O} - H}$$

SIMULTANEOUS BOND MAKING AND BREAKING **85**

49. An important step in the production of acetals occurs when a molecule of alcohol undergoes reaction with the protonated carbonyl group of an aldehyde. A pair of_____electrons on the _____ atom of the alcohol is pushed toward the carbonyl-carbon atom. The pair of _____ electrons of the carbon-oxygen double bond is pushed toward the _____ atom. Thus, a sigma bond is made between oxygen and _____ and a pi bond has been broken between carbon and _____. The oxygen atom of the alcohol, which was neutral, now possesses a _____ charge. The oxygen atom of the protonated aldehyde, which had a positive charge, is now_____.

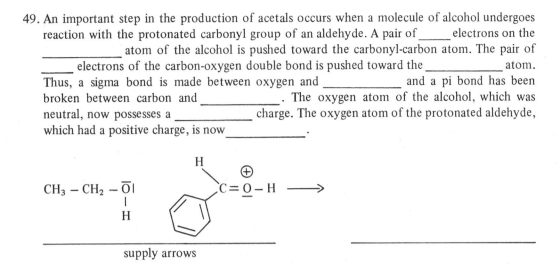

supply arrows

50. The acid-catalyzed hydrolysis of nitriles involves this kind of reaction on a triple bond.

$$\left\langle\!\!\!\bigcirc\!\!\!\right\rangle - CH_2 - C \equiv \overset{\oplus}{N} - H \longrightarrow$$

$$|\overline{O} - H$$
$$|$$
$$H$$

supply arrows

* * * * *

We have seen a number of examples of the simultaneous sigma bond making – pi bond breaking type of reaction where the pushable electrons were n electrons. In many mechanisms one encounters steps in which there is simultaneous sigma bond making and pi bond breaking where it is the pi electrons that are pushed.

$$\overset{\oplus}{E} \quad C = X \longrightarrow E - \overset{|}{\underset{|}{C}} - \overset{\oplus}{X}$$

Once again, an ion and a molecule condense into a single ion. The electrons being pushed are the pi electrons of an unsaturated system. The receptor is an electrophile, usually possessing a formal positive charge. Pushing the pi electrons to the electrophile results in the E–C sigma bond and breaks the pi bond. A formal positive charge is left on the atom X, thus conserving the charge in the system.

In a typical Friedel-Crafts alkylation of benzene, a *t*-butyl cation reacts with a molecule of benzene. A pair of pi electrons from the aromatic ring is pushed toward the positively charged carbon atom of the *t*-butyl cation. Thus, a pi bond between carbon and carbon is broken and a sigma bond between carbon and carbon is made. The positively charged carbon atom of the *t*-butyl cation is now <u>neutral</u>. The carbon atom, *from which the pi electrons departed,* now possesses a <u>positive</u> charge.

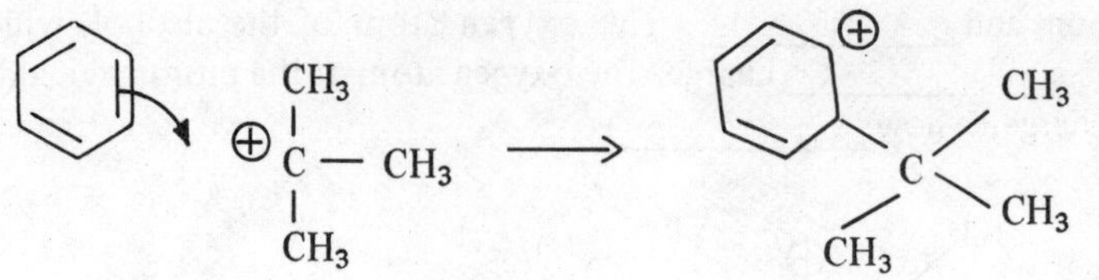

(See footnote 2.)

51. Consider the alkylation of *p*-xylene by an isopropyl cation. A pair of _____ electrons from the aromatic ring is pushed toward the positively charged carbon atom of the isopropyl cation. Thus, a pi bond is broken between carbon and _____, and a sigma bond is made between carbon and _____. The positively charged carbon atom of the isopropyl cation is now _____. The carbon atom, from which the pi electrons departed, now possesses a _____ charge.

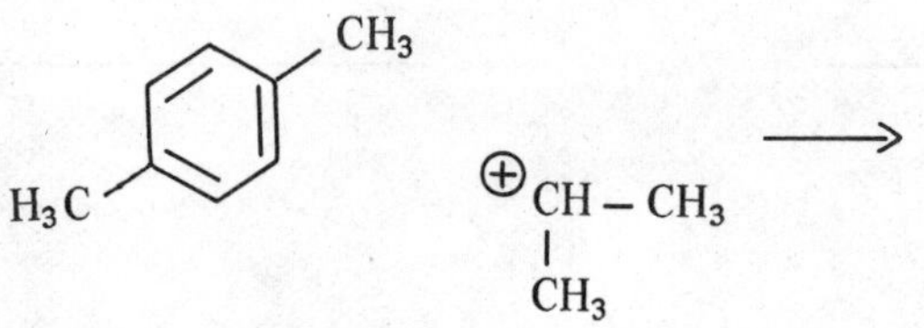

_____
supply arrow

_____

52. The condensation step in the dimerization of isobutylene is very similar. The pi electrons of the double bond in an isobutylene molecule are pushed toward the *t*-butyl cation. However, there are two ways in which this can be done. One way results in a tertiary cation; thus,

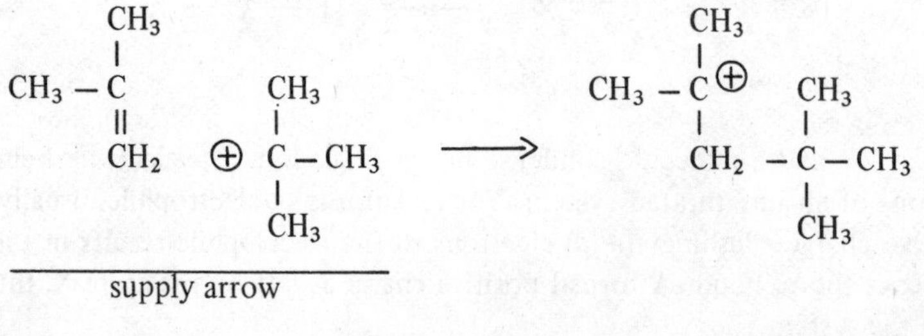

_____
supply arrow

---

[2] Here we see why it is necessary to preserve the Kekulé structure for benzene (Chapter 2). For clarity it is expedient to push electrons in pairs and that is how it is done above. The reaction, as it actually occurs, is quite a complicated affair involving the entire pi system of the benzene ring.

Another way results in a primary cation; thus,

$$CH_3 - \underset{\underset{CH_2}{\overset{\overset{CH_3}{|}}{\parallel}}}{C} \quad \overset{\oplus}{} \underset{\underset{CH_3}{|}}{\overset{\overset{CH_3}{|}}{C}} - CH_3 \qquad \longrightarrow$$

_____   _____
supply arrow

The stabilities of the resulting carbocation (actually, the stabilities of the transition states) is the factor which determines that the former process predominates.

53. It is convenient to view protonation of a pi system as occurring by this simple process. Thus, a pair of _____ electrons from 2-butene is pushed toward the proton. A carbon-_____ pi bond has been broken and a carbon-_____ sigma bond has been made. The proton, which had a positive charge, is now _____. The carbon atom from which the pi electrons departed now possesses a _____ charge.

$$CH_3 - CH = CH - CH_3$$

$$H \overset{\oplus}{} \qquad \longrightarrow$$

_____   _____
supply arrow

54. The protonation of 1-methylcyclohexene occurs in a similar fashion. Here you must make the proper choice between making a bond between the proton and C_1 or C_2.

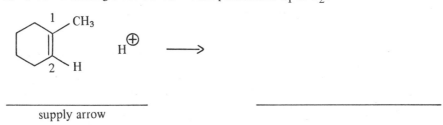

_____   _____
supply arrow

However, as will be shown in a later section, protonation is usually more complicated since it is inaccurate to propose an uncombined proton as a viable species.

PI BOND MAKING – SIGMA BOND BREAKING

There are many steps in organic reaction mechanisms where a pi bond is formed at the same time that a sigma bond is broken. Each of the reactions in the preceding section, when written in reverse, provides an example of this process. Thus,

$$Nu - \underset{|}{\overset{|}{C}} - \overset{\ominus}{\bar{X}} \longrightarrow \overset{\ominus}{\bar{Nu}} \qquad \overset{\diagdown}{\diagup} C = X$$

The pushable electrons are the n electrons on the atom X. As they are pushed toward the carbon atom to form a pi bond the sigma electrons which form the Nu — C bond leave with Nu. Charge is conserved as Nu leaves as an anion.

Consider the fate of the ion formed from the attack of hydroxide ion on ethyl acetate. If one of the pairs of n electrons on the negatively charged oxygen atom is pushed toward carbon to reform the carbonyl pi bond, and the sigma bond between carbon and the OH group is broken, we have exactly reversed the reaction by which the ion was formed.

$$CH_3 - C(\overline{|O|}^{\ominus}) - \overline{O} - CH_2 - CH_3 \quad\longrightarrow\quad CH_3 - C(\overline{O|}) - \overline{O} - CH_2 - CH_3 \qquad ^{\ominus}|\overline{O} - H$$

This step does occur. However, since it does not lead toward the products of saponification, namely, carboxylate anion and alcohol, we shall consider another fate for the ion.

55. If, as the n electrons are being used to reform the carbonyl pi bond, the sigma bond between the carbon and the — $\overline{O}$ — CH_2 — CH_3 group is broken we get something that looks like progress toward products. Thus, a pi bond has been made between oxygen and _____ and a sigma bond has been broken between carbon and _____.

$$CH_3 - C(\overline{|O|}^{\ominus})(|\overline{O} - H) - \overline{O} - CH_2 - CH_3 \quad\longrightarrow$$

_____ supply arrows _____

The simple transfer of a proton from the carboxylic acid to the alcoholate anion leads to the saponification products.

56. The final step in the benzoin condensation involves the making of a pi bond between oxygen and carbon and the breaking of the sigma bond between carbon and the CN group. That is:

benzoin structure with CN, C, CH, $^{\ominus}|O|$, $|O-H$ groups $\quad\longrightarrow$

_____ supply arrows _____ .

*   *   *   *   *

Another general form that these steps can take involves the expulsion of a neutral nucleophile.

$$^{\oplus}Nu - C - \overline{X} \quad\longrightarrow\quad \overline{N}u \quad C = X^{\oplus}$$

57. The cleavage step in the acid-catalyzed hydrolysis of esters provides a good example. A pair of n electrons from one of the OH groups is pushed toward the <u>carbon</u> atom. Simultaneously, the pair of <u>sigma</u> electrons is pushed toward the positively charged oxygen atom. Thus, a pi bond is made between oxygen and _____ and a sigma bond is broken between carbon and _____ . The neutral oxygen atom from which the pi electrons were pushed now possesses a _____ charge. The positively charged oxygen toward which the electrons were pushed is now _____ .

$$CH_3 - \overset{\overset{\displaystyle |\overline{O} - H}{|}}{\underset{\underset{\displaystyle |O - H}{|}}{C}} - \overset{\oplus}{\underset{\underset{\displaystyle }{}}{O}} - CH_2 - CH_3 \longrightarrow CH_3 - \overset{\overset{\displaystyle \overset{\oplus}{\overline{O}} - H}{||}}{\underset{\underset{\displaystyle |O - H}{|}}{C}} \qquad \overset{\overset{\displaystyle H}{|}}{|O} - CH_2 - CH_3$$

Here, the resulting conjugate acid of acetic acid loses a proton to complete the hydrolytic mechanism.

58. Similarly, the penultimate step in the hydrolysis of an acetal is the loss of a methanol molecule from:

$$R - \overset{\overset{\displaystyle |\overline{O} - H}{|}}{\underset{\underset{\displaystyle R}{|}}{C}} - \overset{\oplus}{\underset{\underset{\displaystyle H}{|}}{\overline{O}}} - CH_3 \qquad \longrightarrow$$

_____   _____ .
  supply arrows

*   *   *   *   *

The examples of simultaneous pi bond formation and sigma bond breaking that we have seen so far have occurred when a pair of n electrons was pushed to form the pi bonds, and a nucleophile, either neutral or negatively charged, was expelled. Another way in which a pi bond can be formed when a sigma bond is broken is to push a pair of sigma electrons in such a way as to form the pi bond. In these cases a positively charged fragment is lost. Thus,

$$E - \overset{\overset{\displaystyle |}{}}{\underset{\underset{\displaystyle |}{}}{C}} - \overset{\oplus}{X} \longrightarrow E^{\oplus} \qquad \overset{}{\diagdown}C = X \quad .$$

Most commonly, this occurs when a proton is lost from some positively charged intermediate.

59. The *t*-butyl cation can lose a proton and form the neutral molecule, isobutylene. Thus, a pair of sigma electrons forming a <u>carbon-hydrogen</u> bond is pushed toward the positively charged carbon atom. The sigma bond between hydrogen and _____ is broken, and a pi bond is formed between carbon and _____ . The neutral hydrogen atom now possesses a _____ charge. The positively charged carbon atom is now _____ .

$$CH_3 - \overset{\overset{\displaystyle H_2C - H}{|}}{\underset{\underset{\displaystyle CH_3}{|}}{\overset{\oplus}{C}}} \longrightarrow CH_3 - \overset{\overset{\displaystyle H_2C}{||}}{\underset{\underset{\displaystyle CH_3}{|}}{C}} \qquad H^{\oplus}$$

60. Similarly, a proton can be lost from *sec*-butyl cation to form 2-butene. A pair of sigma electrons which form the hydrogen-carbon bond is pushed toward the positively charged _____ atom. The sigma bond between hydrogen and _____ is broken, and a pi bond between carbon and _____ is made. The neutral hydrogen atom now possesses a _____ charge. The positively charged carbon atom is now_____.

$$CH_3 - \overset{\displaystyle \oplus}{CH} - \underset{\displaystyle \underset{|}{H}}{CH} - CH_3 \longrightarrow$$

_____   _____
        supply arrow

61. Consider the loss of a proton from the carbocation below. This intermediate could lose a primary hydrogen giving the terminal olefin, 2,4,4-trimethyl-1-pentene,

$$\underset{\displaystyle H}{\overset{\displaystyle }{CH_2}} - \underset{\displaystyle \oplus}{\overset{\displaystyle CH_3}{C}} - CH_2 - \underset{\displaystyle CH_3}{\overset{\displaystyle CH_3}{C}} - CH_3 \longrightarrow$$

_____   _____
        supply arrow

or it could lose a secondary hydrogen and become 2,4,4-trimethyl-2-pentene,

$$CH_3 - \underset{\displaystyle \oplus}{\overset{\displaystyle CH_3}{C}} - \underset{\displaystyle H}{\overset{\displaystyle }{CH}} - \underset{\displaystyle CH_3}{\overset{\displaystyle CH_3}{C}} - CH_3 \longrightarrow$$

_____   _____.
        supply arrow

The latter process predominates since the olefin formed is more stable.

The reformation of the aromatic system in the last step of electrophilic aromatic-substitution involves this type of process.

62. In the final step of the chlorination of benzene, the positively charged intermediate loses a proton from the carbon atom to which a chlorine atom has been attached. The pair of sigma electrons which form the bond between carbon and hydrogen is pushed toward the positively charged carbon atom. The result is the breaking of a hydrogen-_____ sigma bond, and the making of a carbon-_____ pi bond. (The 6-pi electron aromatic system is restored.) The neutral hydrogen atom now possesses a _____ charge and the positively charged carbon atom is now _____.

63. The final step in the nitration of toluene is similar.

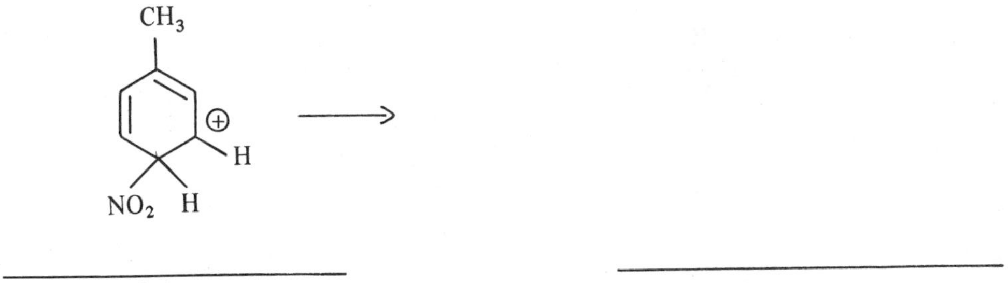

supply arrow

64. Also, the final step in the bromination of *m*-xylene.

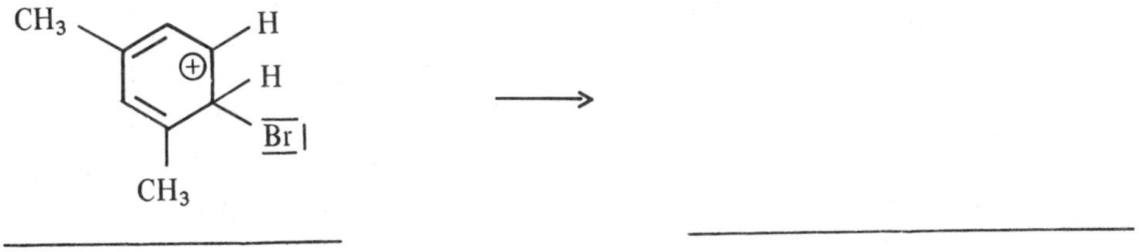

supply arrow

65. On rare occasions a *t*-butyl group is lost in electrophilic aromatic substitution.

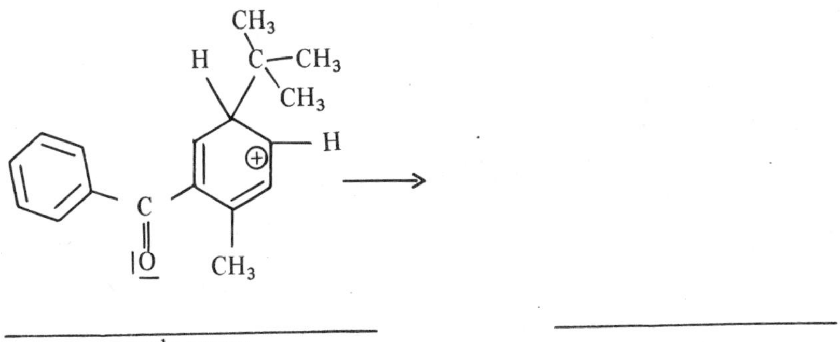

supply arrow

66. Finally, the loss of a proton from the conjugate acid of a carbonyl group is often found as the final step in a reaction mechanism.

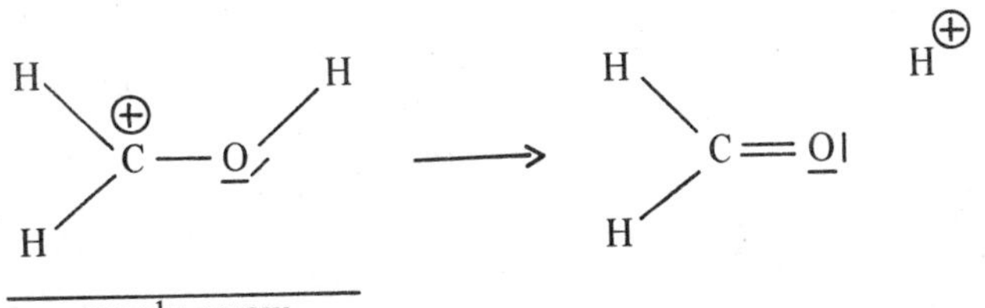

supply arrow

67. Similarly,

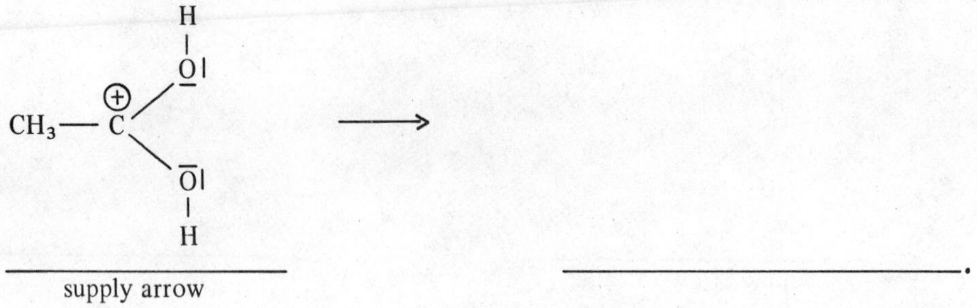

$$CH_3 - \overset{\oplus}{\underset{\overset{|}{\underset{H}{\overset{|}{\underset{}{O}}}}}{\overset{\overset{H}{|}}{\overset{\overset{|}{O}}{}}}}{C} \longrightarrow$$

supply arrow

Exercises

Where arrows are supplied write in the products, where the products are written supply the appropriate arrows.

68.

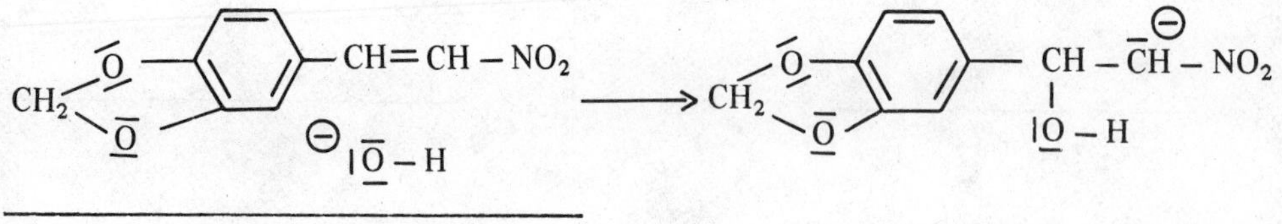

69.

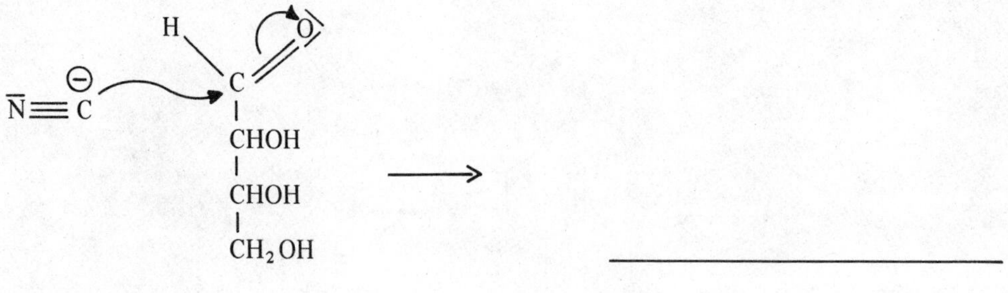

70.

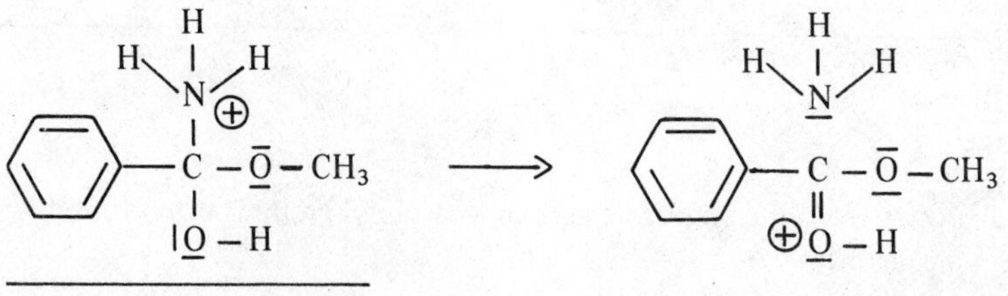

71.

72.

73.

74.

75.

76.

77.

78.

79.

80.

COMPLEX MECHANISMS

When dealing with electron pushing in this Chapter, we have, until now, illustrated steps in reaction mechanisms with examples in which the making and breaking of no more than two bonds occurs in any step. The awful truth is that there are many examples which are more complex. We shall take up some of them in this section. It should be emphasized that these steps are more complicated in numbers of electron pairs being pushed, but the types of bond making and bond breaking should all be familiar by this time.

The E2 elimination is a reaction in which everything happens at once. In the example below a base abstracts a proton *beta* to the leaving group. The electrons which had formed the C − H bond are pushed toward the *alpha* carbon from which, in turn, the leaving group departs taking with it the pair of electrons which had formed the C – X bond. All of this happens more or less simultaneously. Inspection reveals that this process involves sigma bond making, sigma bond breaking, pi bond making and sigma bond breaking.

81. In the formation of 2-butene from 2-bromobutane a pair of n electrons from the oxygen atom of hydroxide ion is pushed toward the beta hydrogen forming an oxygen-hydrogen bond. The pair of sigma electrons which was the hydrogen-carbon bond is pushed toward the alpha carbon atom forming a pi bond between carbon and carbon. The sigma electrons of the carbon-bromine bond are pushed toward the bromine atom. The hydroxyl oxygen which had a negative charge is now neutral and the bromine atom which was neutral now has a negative charge.

supply arrows

82. In the reaction of ethoxide ion with *t*-butyl chloride a pair of n electrons on the oxygen atom of ethoxide ion is pushed toward the beta hydrogen forming an oxygen-_____ bond. The pair of sigma electrons which was the hydrogen-carbon bond is pushed toward the alpha carbon forming a pi bond between carbon and _____. The sigma electrons of the carbon-chlorine bond are pushed toward the chlorine atom. The ethoxyl oxygen which had a negative charge is now _____. The chlorine which was neutral now has a _____ charge.

supply arrows

83. Here is an example of an E2 reaction forming a double bond in a ring.

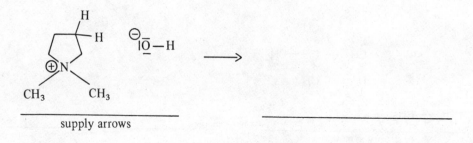

CH₃ H

H

$\overline{\underline{C}l}\,|$

CH₃—CH₂ H

⊖
$|\overline{\underline{O}}$—H

——————————————   ——————————————
supply arrows

84. The Hofmann elimination is a similar reaction except that the charge distribution is different. The hydroxyl oxygen which had a negative charge becomes _____ and the nitrogen which had a positive charge becomes _____.

CH₃
|⊕
CH₃—N—CH₃
|
CH₂—CH—CH₂—CH₃   ⟶
|
H

H—$\overline{\underline{O}}|$ ⊖

——————————————   ——————————————
supply arrows

85. Here is a Hofmann elimination in which a double bond is formed in the ring.

H ⊕
—N(CH₃)₃

—H

H ⊖
$|\overline{\underline{O}}$—CH₂—CH₃

——————————————   ——————————————
supply arrows

86. Finally the Hofmann elimination can result in a ring-opening reaction.

H

—H   ⊖
$|\overline{\underline{O}}$—H   ⟶

⊕N

CH₃   CH₃

——————————————   ——————————————
supply arrows

87. When a chlorine molecule interacts with a carbon-carbon double bond the result is a carbocation. The pi electrons of the carbon-carbon double bond are mobilized to form a carbon-chlorine sigma bond. In turn, the sigma electrons of the chlorine-chlorine bond are pushed so that chloride ion departs. This process involves pi bond breaking, sigma bond making, and sigma bond breaking.

$$1 \quad 2 \quad 3 \quad 4$$

$$CH_3 - CH = CH - CH_3 \longrightarrow CH_3 - \underset{\oplus}{CH} - CH - CH_3$$
$$|\overline{Cl} - \overline{Cl}| \qquad\qquad |\underline{Cl}| \quad |\overline{Cl}|^{\ominus}$$

_____
supply arrows

The carbon atom, C_2, from which the pi electrons depart obtains a _____ charge and the chlorine atom to which the electrons are pushed obtains a _____ charge.

88. An undissociated acid protonates a carbon-carbon double bond in an analogous fashion.

_____
supply arrows

89. Another example is:

_____
supply arrows

* * * * *

When the carbon-carbon double bond is unsymmetrical, this type of reaction can lead to two different carbocation intermediates. The choice of which one is preferred is determined by the relative stabilities of the carbocations.

90. The protonation of propylene by hydrogen chloride can lead to two different carbocations. If, as the pi bond breaks, the new sigma bond is made between C_1 and the hydrogen atom, a secondary carbocation is formed.

$$3 \quad 2 \quad 1$$

$$CH_3 - CH = CH_2 \longrightarrow CH_3 - \overset{\oplus}{CH} - CH_2$$
$$H - \overline{Cl}| \qquad\qquad H \qquad |\overline{Cl}|^{\ominus}$$

However, if the new sigma bond is made between C_2 and the hydrogen atom a primary carbocation is formed.

$$\overset{3}{C}H_3 - \overset{2}{C}H = \overset{1}{C}H_2 \longrightarrow$$

$$H - \overline{\underline{C}l}|$$

_____

Because the transition state leading to the secondary carbocation is more stable, the first of these two products is formed preferentially.

91. When hydrogen iodide is allowed to react with isobutylene, two carbocations can form. If the new sigma bond is formed between C_1 and the hydrogen atom a tertiary carbocation results.

$$\overset{3}{C}H_3 - \overset{2}{\underset{\underset{CH_3}{|}}{C}} = \overset{1}{C}H_2 \longrightarrow$$

$$H - \overline{\underline{I}}|$$

_____
supply arrows   _____

However, if the new sigma bond is formed between C_2 and the hydrogen atom, a primary carbocation is produced.

$$\overset{3}{C}H_3 - \overset{2}{\underset{\underset{CH_3}{|}}{C}} = \overset{1}{C}H_2 \longrightarrow$$

$$H - \overline{\underline{I}}|$$

_____
supply arrows   _____

The first of these two is preferred.

92. The reaction of bromine with styrene can yield a secondary, benzylic carbocation.

$$\langle\!\!\bigcirc\!\!\rangle - CH = CH_2 \longrightarrow$$

$$|\overline{\underline{B}}r - \overline{\underline{B}}r|$$

_____
supply arrows   _____

or, a primary carbocation,

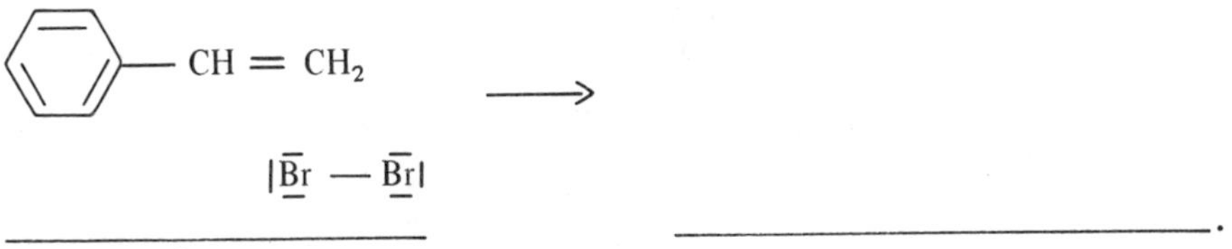

supply arrows

The first reaction is preferred.

Exercises

Here are some steps in organic mechanisms. In cases where arrows are supplied write the products taking particular care about formal charge. In cases where products are given supply the appropriate arrows.

93.

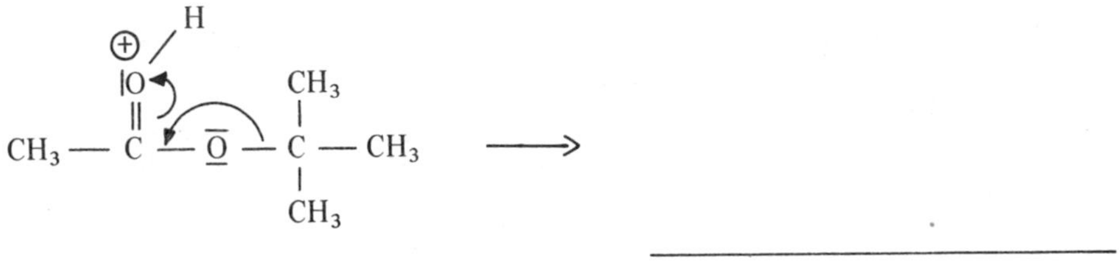

94.

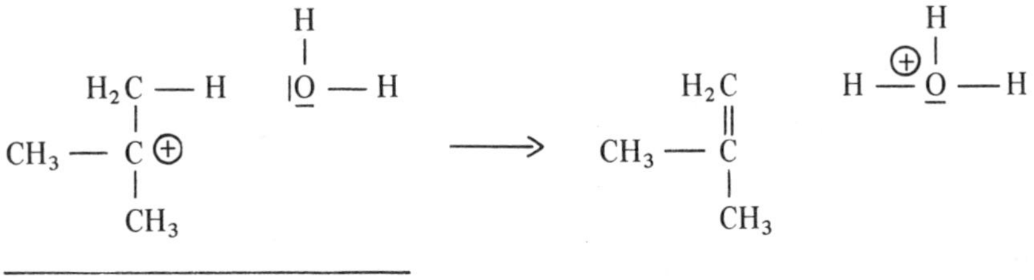

95.

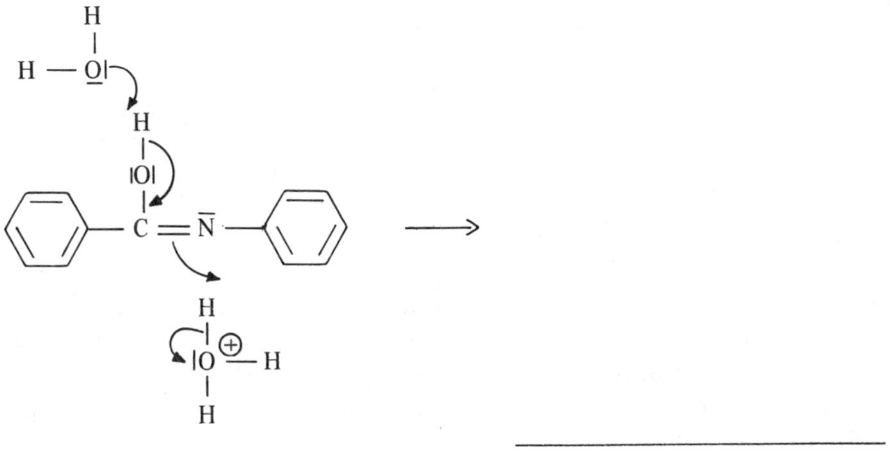

96.

97.

98.

99.

REARRANGEMENTS

The group of reactions in which rearrangements occur is one feature that lends organic chemistry its attractiveness and uniqueness. For some, figuring out what happened during a rearrangement presents a stimulating challenge; for others, it is a complete mystery. In all cases the rearrangement can be figured out by pushing electrons properly and by carefully keeping the relative positions of the atoms straight.

The first, and most common, rearrangements encountered in the study of organic chemistry are 1,2-shifts in carbocations. In these reactions, a group (Y) one carbon atom away from a carbocation center moves, with its pair of electrons, to that center. The carbon atom from which that group migrated is left with a formal positive charge. Thus,

$$\underset{|}{\overset{Y}{\underset{|}{C}}} - \overset{\oplus}{\underset{|}{C}} - \quad \longrightarrow \quad \overset{\oplus}{\underset{|}{C}} - \underset{|}{\overset{Y}{\underset{|}{C}}} - \quad .$$

In this general example the pushable electrons are the sigma electrons of the C − Y bond and the receptor is the positively charged carbon atom. The driving force for these 1,2-shifts is usually the formation of a more stable carbocation. The groups which most often take the role of Y are hydrogen, methyl, and aryl.

The 1-butyl cation suffers a 1,2-hydride shift to become the more stable 2-butyl cation. A neighboring hydrogen atom, with its pair of sigma electrons, migrates to the positively charged carbon atom which becomes neutral. The neutral carbon atom from which the hydride ion migrated obtains a positive charge.

$$CH_3 - CH_2 - \underset{\underset{H}{|}}{CH} - \overset{\oplus}{CH_2} \quad \longrightarrow \quad CH_3 - CH_2 - \overset{\oplus}{CH} - \underset{\underset{H}{|}}{CH_2}$$

100. The isobutyl cation rearranges *via* a hydride shift to the *t*-butyl cation.

$$CH_3 - \underset{\underset{H}{|}}{\overset{\overset{CH_3}{|}}{C}} - \overset{\oplus}{CH_2} \quad \longrightarrow$$

_____   _____
           supply arrow

101. A 1,2-shift of a methyl group is illustrated in the rearrangement of the 3,3-dimethyl-2-butyl cation to the 2,3-dimethyl-2-butyl cation.

$$CH_3 - \underset{\underset{CH_3}{|}}{\overset{\overset{CH_3}{|}}{C}} - \overset{\oplus}{CH} - CH_3 \quad \longrightarrow$$

                                          _____

102. Similarly,

$$CH_3 - \underset{\underset{CH_3}{|}}{\overset{\overset{CH_3}{|}}{C}} - \overset{\oplus}{CH_2} \quad \longrightarrow$$

_____   _____
           supply arrow

*   *   *   *   *

In each of the cases above the rearrangement resulted in the formation of a more stable cation, that is, a secondary and tertiary cation are formed from a primary, and another tertiary cation is formed from a secondary. Very often one must choose the most likely rearrangement from among several alternatives.

103. The 1-propyl cation can rearrange *via* either a 1,2-hydride shift or a 1,2-methyl shift. The 1,2-hydride shift leads to the more stable isopropyl cation.

$$
\begin{array}{c}
\quad\quad\ \text{H} \\
\quad\quad\ | \\
\text{H} - \text{C} - \overset{\oplus}{\text{CH}_2} \\
\quad\quad\ | \\
\quad\quad\ \text{CH}_3
\end{array}
\quad\longrightarrow
$$

_____   _____
supply arrow

A 1,2-methyl shift is not as likely because it would yield a primary cation as the product of rearrangement.

104. The most likely rearrangement for the 2-methyl-1-butyl cation is:

$$
\begin{array}{c}
\quad\quad\quad\quad\quad\ \text{CH}_3 \\
\quad\quad\quad\quad\quad\ | \quad\ \oplus \\
\text{CH}_3 - \text{CH}_2 - \text{C} - \text{CH}_2 \\
\quad\quad\quad\quad\quad\ | \\
\quad\quad\quad\quad\quad\ \text{H}
\end{array}
\quad\longrightarrow
$$

_____   _____ .
supply arrow

105. In the cation below there are three different groups (hydrogen on C_1, hydrogen on C_3, or methyl on C_3) which can shift to give three possible products of rearrangement. The most likely rearrangement is:

$$
\begin{array}{c}
\quad\quad\quad\ \text{CH}_3 \\
\quad\quad\quad\ | \quad\ \oplus \\
\text{CH}_3 - \text{C} - \text{CH} - \text{CH}_2 \\
\ \ 4 \quad\ 3 | \quad 2 \quad\ 1 | \\
\quad\quad\quad\ \text{H} \quad\quad\quad \text{H}
\end{array}
\quad\longrightarrow
$$

_____   _____ .
supply arrow

106. A 1,2-methyl shift occurs in the pinacol-pinacolone rearrangement.

$$
\begin{array}{c}
\quad\quad\quad\ \text{CH}_3 \\
\quad\quad\quad\ | \quad\ \oplus \\
\text{CH}_3 - \text{C} - \text{C} - \text{CH}_3 \\
\quad\quad\quad\ | \quad\ | \\
\quad\quad\quad\ |\underline{\text{O}}\text{H} \quad \text{CH}_3
\end{array}
\quad\longrightarrow
$$

_____   _____
supply arrow

107. Groups can migrate from one position on a ring to another.

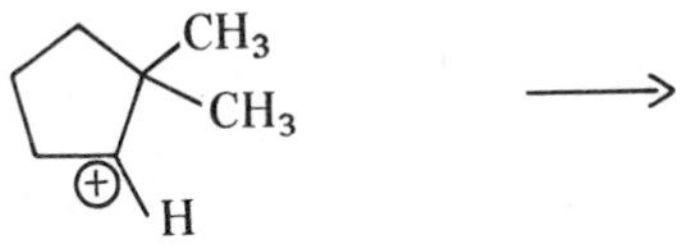

supply arrow

108. When a phenyl group is found next to a cationic center there is a strong possibility that it will migrate. For example:

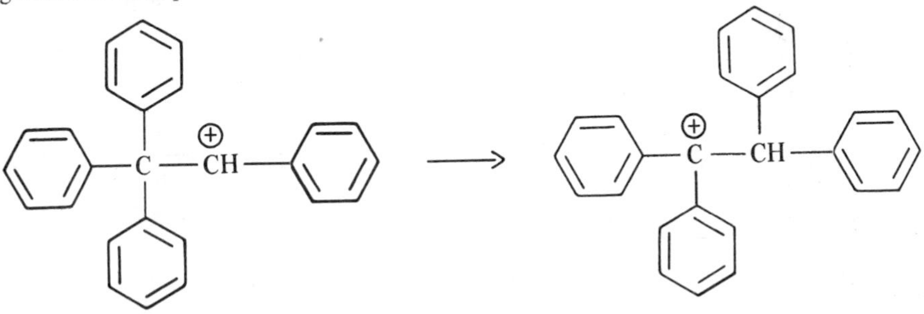

supply arrow

109. Phenyl groups can migrate from one position on a ring to another.

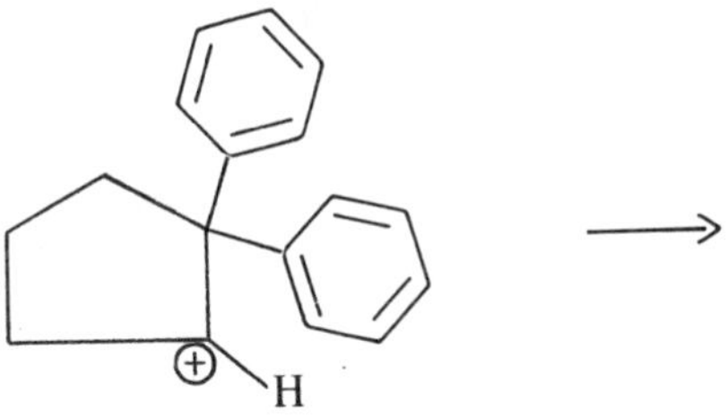

supply arrow

110. Phenyl groups migrate in the pinacol-pinacolone type rearrangements.

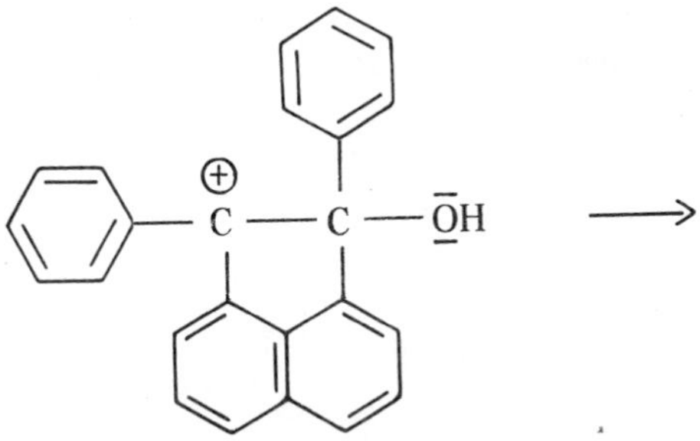

supply arrow

111. Electron releasing substituents on the aryl ring tend to make that ring migrate in preference to an unsubstituted phenyl group. In the reaction below, the *para*-anisyl group migrates in preference to phenyl.

$$\text{(structure: triphenyl-type carbon center)}\quad\text{C}\!-\!\overset{\oplus}{\text{CH}}\!-\!\text{CH}_2\!-\!\text{CH}_3 \longrightarrow$$

with aryl groups: two phenyl rings and one *para*-substituted ring bearing $|\underline{\text{O}}-\text{CH}_3$

———————————— supply arrow ————————————

112. Electron attracting groups have the opposite effect so that phenyl migrates in preference to *para*-chlorophenyl.

$$\text{(structure: triphenyl-type carbon center)}\quad\text{C}\!-\!\overset{\oplus}{\text{CH}}\!-\!\text{CH}_2\!-\!\text{CH}_3 \longrightarrow$$

with aryl groups: two phenyl rings and one *para*-substituted ring bearing $|\text{Cl}\,|$

———————————— supply arrow ————————————

Exercises

Here are some carbocations which can be expected to rearrange *via* 1,2-shifts. Show the rearrangement which is most probable.

113.

$$\text{H}_3\text{C}-\underset{\underset{\displaystyle \text{CH}_3}{|}}{\overset{\overset{\displaystyle \text{CH}_3}{|}}{\text{C}}}-\overset{\oplus}{\text{CH}}-\underset{\underset{\displaystyle \text{CH}_3}{|}}{\overset{\overset{\displaystyle \text{H}}{|}}{\text{C}}}-\text{H} \longrightarrow$$

————————————   ————————————

114.

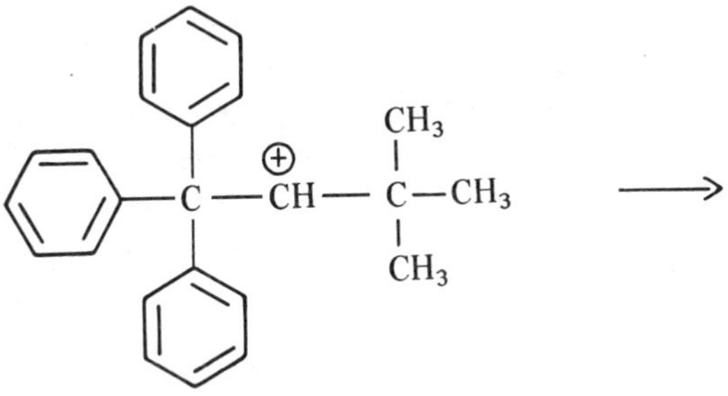

CH_3

C — CH — C — CH_3

CH_3

⟶

_____   _____

115.

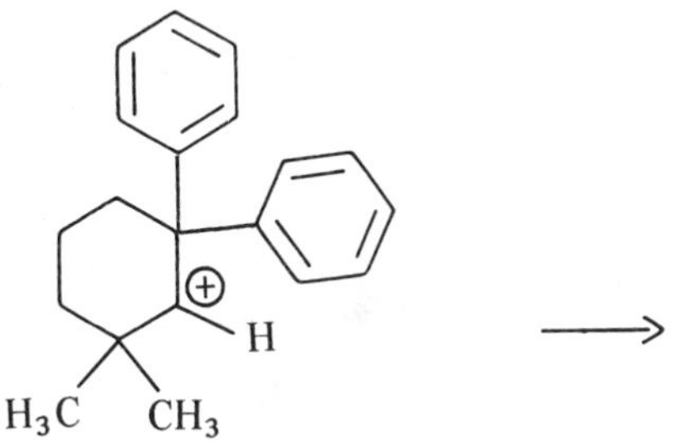

H_3C CH_3 H

⟶

_____   _____

116.

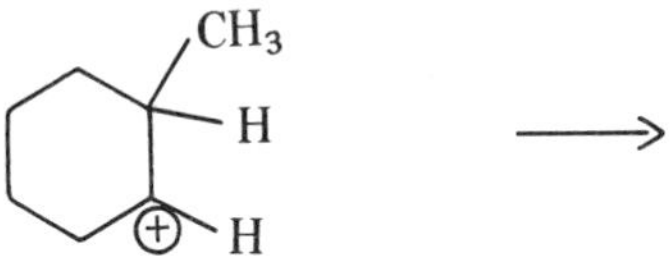

CH_3

H

H

⟶

_____   _____

117.

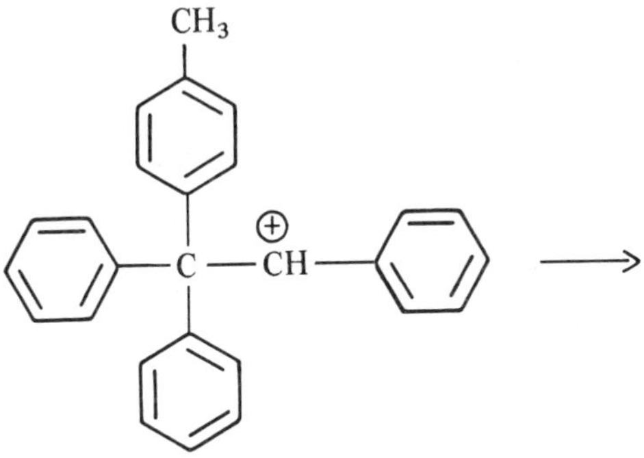

CH_3

C — CH

⟶

_____   _____

118.

CN

C — CH

⟶

_____   _____

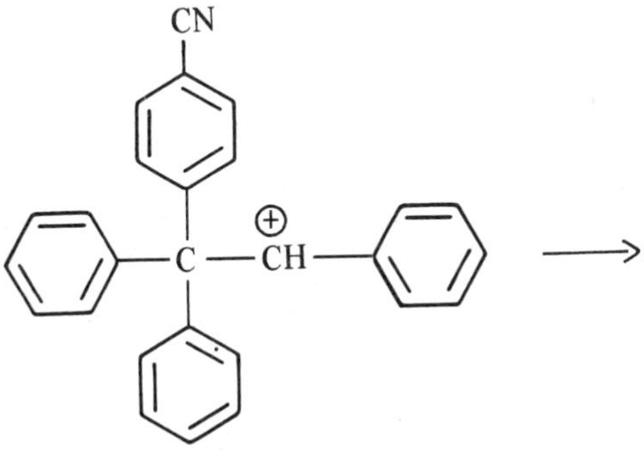

*   *   *   *   *

Another 1,2-shift involving carbocations is very similar to the rearrangements we have already seen. However, it often tortures students because it involves ring expansion or ring contraction which are difficult to see at first. In the general example below, a carbocation outside the ring is a receptor for a migrating methylene group. The result of such a migration is, inevitably, a ring containing one more carbon than the original ring. The positive charge is now on a carbon atom in the ring.

The cyclohexylmethyl cation rearranges by expanding to the cycloheptyl cation. The author has found it useful to show the rearrangement of the bonds while keeping the positions of the atoms constant. Then, after the rearrangement has been shown, the structure can be altered to a more familiar form.

119. The cyclopropylmethyl cation suffers a similar rearrangement.

_____   _____

120. Similarly, the cyclobutylmethyl cation undergoes a ring expansion.

_____   _____   _____
   supply arrow

121. Another example is:

_____   _____   _____
   supply arrow

*   *   *   *   *

Alternatively, the carbocation center can be inside the ring. In this case the migration of a methylene group leads to a ring contraction. The ring will contain one less member than the original ring and the positive charge will be on a carbon atom outside the ring.

The 2,2-dimethyl-cyclohexyl cation undergoes a ring contracting rearrangement. Once again it is useful to keep the atoms in the same position as the bonds are rearranged.

122. The cyclopentyl cation will contract to the cyclobutylmethyl cation.

$\equiv$

_____   _____   _____
supply arrow

123. Another example is:

$\equiv$

_____   _____   _____
supply arrow

124. A slight variation on this reaction occurs when cyclopropyl cations rearrange to form allyl cations. Scrutiny of this process will show it to be like a ring contraction process, the double bond being comparable to a two-membered ring.

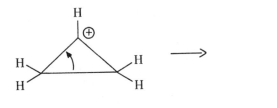

_____

125. Another example is:

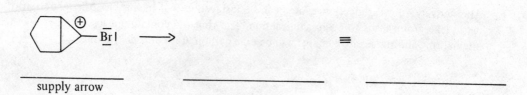

_____
supply arrow

ANSWERS

CHAPTER 3

1. chloride, carbon-chlorine, chlorine, negative, positive, isopropyl,

$$H - \overset{\overset{\displaystyle CH_3}{|}}{\underset{\underset{\displaystyle CH_3}{|}}{C}} \oplus \qquad |\overline{\underline{C}l}|^{\ominus}$$

2. bromide, carbon-bromine, bromine, negative, positive, bromide, cyclohexyl,

(cyclohexyl) $\curvearrowleft \overline{\underline{B}r}| \longrightarrow$ (cyclohexyl) $\oplus$ $\qquad |\overline{\underline{B}r}|^{\ominus}$

3.

$$CH_3 - \overset{\overset{\displaystyle CH_3}{|}}{\underset{\underset{\displaystyle CH_3}{|}}{C}} \overset{\curvearrowleft}{\underset{\underset{\displaystyle H}{|}}{\overset{\oplus}{\overline{O}}}} - H \longrightarrow CH_3 - \overset{\overset{\displaystyle CH_3}{|}}{\underset{\underset{\displaystyle CH_3}{|}}{C}} \oplus \qquad \overset{\overline{}}{\underset{\underset{\displaystyle H}{|}}{\overline{O}}} - H$$

4. oxygen, neutral, positive,

$$CH_3 - \overline{\underline{O}} - CH_2 \overset{\curvearrowleft}{-} \overset{\oplus}{\underset{\underset{\displaystyle H}{|}}{\overline{O}}} - \overset{\overset{\displaystyle \overline{O}|}{\|}}{C} - CH_3 \longrightarrow CH_3 - \overline{\underline{O}} - CH_2 \quad \overset{}{\underset{\underset{\displaystyle H}{|}}{|\overline{O}}} - \overset{\overset{\displaystyle \overline{O}|}{\|}}{C} - CH_3$$

5. oxygen positive, neutral, positive,

$$CH_3 - \overset{\overset{\displaystyle CH_3}{|}}{C}$$
$$\qquad \overline{O} - H$$
$$CH_3 - \overset{}{\underset{\underset{\displaystyle CH_3}{|}}{C}} \overset{\curvearrowleft}{\oplus}$$

6.

(phenyl)$-CH_2 \overset{\curvearrowright}{-} \overline{\underline{B}r}| \longrightarrow$ (phenyl)$-\overset{\oplus}{C}H_2$ $\qquad |\overline{\underline{B}r}|^{\ominus}$

7.

$|\overline{\underline{C}}l \overset{\curvearrowleft}{-} CH$ (diphenyl) $\longrightarrow |\overline{\underline{C}}l|^{\ominus}$ $\overset{\oplus}{C}H$ (diphenyl)

8.

9. $CH_3 - \overline{O} - \langle\text{ring}\rangle - CH_2 - \underline{\overline{C}l| \longrightarrow CH_3\overline{O} - \langle\text{ring}\rangle - \overset{\oplus}{CH_2}$ $|\underline{\overline{C}l|^{\ominus}}$

10.

11.

12.

13.

14.

15. n, bromide, carbon, bromine, sigma, negative, neutral, positive, neutral

$$CH_3-CH_2-\overset{\overset{\displaystyle CH_3}{|}}{\underset{\underset{\displaystyle H}{|}}{C}}\overset{\oplus}{}\quad|\overline{Br}|^{\ominus} \longrightarrow CH_3-CH_2-\overset{\overset{\displaystyle CH_3}{|}}{\underset{\underset{\displaystyle H}{|}}{C}}-\overline{Br}|$$

16.

17. n, nitrogen, carbon, sigma, positive, positive, neutral,

18.

19.

20.

21.

22.

23. hydroxide, chloride, n, sigma, chlorine, carbon, chlorine, neutral, negative,

$$H-\overline{\underset{..}{O}}|^{\ominus} \quad CH_2-\overline{\underset{..}{Cl}}| \longrightarrow H-\overline{\underset{..}{O}}-CH_2 \qquad |\overline{\underset{..}{Cl}}|^{\ominus}$$
$$\underset{CH_3}{|} \qquad\qquad\qquad \underset{CH_3}{|}$$

24.

$$H-\overline{\underset{..}{O}}|^{\ominus} \quad CH_2-\overline{\underset{..}{Br}}| \longrightarrow H-\overline{\underset{..}{O}}-CH_2 \qquad |\overline{\underset{..}{Br}}|^{\ominus}$$

(phenyl group attached to CH_2 on both sides)

25. hydrogen, oxygen,

(phenoxide) $-\overline{\underset{..}{O}}|^{\ominus} \qquad H-\overline{\underset{..}{O}}-H$

26. n, nitrogen, sigma, carbon, hydrogen, carbon, neutral, negative,

$$H-C\equiv C-H \quad |\overline{\underset{H}{N}}-H \longrightarrow H-C\equiv \overline{C}|^{\ominus} \quad H-\underset{H}{\overset{|}{N}}-H$$
$$\qquad\qquad |^{\ominus}$$

27.

$$CH_3-CH_2-\overline{\underset{..}{O}}|^{\ominus} \quad H-CH_2-C\overset{\nearrow O|}{\underset{\searrow H}{}} \longrightarrow CH_3-CH_2-\overline{\underset{..}{O}}-H \quad {}^{\ominus}\overline{C}H_2-C\overset{\nearrow O|}{\underset{\searrow H}{}}$$

28. *n*-propyl, n, carbon, sigma, oxygen, oxygen, carbon, oxygen, neutral, negative,

$$CH_3-CH_2-\overline{C}H_2^{\ominus} \quad \overset{CH_2}{\underset{CH_2}{\diagdown \underset{O|}{\diagup}}} \longrightarrow CH_3-CH_2-CH_2-CH_2$$
$$\overset{\oplus}{MgI} \qquad\qquad\qquad \overset{\oplus}{MgI} \qquad \underset{CH_2-\overline{O}|^{\ominus}}{|}$$

29. ethoxide, n, oxygen, carbon, sigma, oxygen, oxygen, carbon, oxygen, neutral, negative,

$$CH_3-CH_2-\overline{\underset{..}{O}}|^{\ominus} \quad \overset{CH_3}{\underset{|}{CH}}\overset{}{\underset{CH}{\overset{\diagdown O|}{\diagup}}} \longrightarrow CH_3-CH_2-\overline{\underset{..}{O}}-\overset{CH_3}{\underset{|}{CH}}$$
$$\qquad\qquad \underset{CH_3}{\underset{|}{CH}} \qquad\qquad\qquad \underset{CH_3}{\underset{|}{CH-\overline{O}|^{\ominus}}}$$

30. cyclohexanol, oxygen, hydronium, n, hydrogen, sigma, oxygen, oxygen, hydrogen, oxygen, positive, neutral,

31. oxygen, anilinium, n, hydrogen, sigma, nitrogen, nitrogen, hydrogen, nitrogen, neutral, positive,

32.

33.

34.

35.

36.

$$CH_3-CH_2-\overset{\oplus}{\underset{|}{\overline{O}}}-H \quad \overset{H}{\underset{|}{\overline{|O}}}-H \longrightarrow CH_3-CH_2-\overline{O}| \quad H-\overset{\oplus}{\underset{|}{\overline{O}}}-H$$

(with phenyl rings attached)

37.

$$\langle C_6H_5\rangle-\overset{\ominus}{\overline{O}}| \quad \overset{CH_3}{\underset{|}{CH_2}}-\overline{I}| \longrightarrow \langle C_6H_5\rangle-\overline{O}-\overset{CH_3}{\underset{|}{CH_2}} \quad |\overset{\ominus}{\overline{I}}|$$

38.

$$\overset{CH_3-CH_2-\overline{O}}{\underset{CH_3}{\diagdown}}C=\overline{O} \quad H-\overline{O}-SO_3H \longrightarrow \overset{CH_3-CH_2-\overline{O}}{\underset{CH_3}{\diagdown}}\overset{\oplus}{C}=\overset{\oplus}{\underset{}{\overline{O}}}-H \quad |\overset{\ominus}{\overline{O}}-SO_3H$$

39.

$$\overset{H}{\underset{C_6H_5}{\diagdown}}\overset{\oplus}{C}=\overset{\oplus}{\overline{O}}-H \quad |\overset{\ominus}{\overline{O}}-\overset{\overline{O}|}{\overset{||}{C}}-CH_3 \longrightarrow \overset{H}{\underset{C_6H_5}{\diagdown}}C=\overline{O}| \quad H-\overline{O}-\overset{\overline{O}|}{\overset{||}{C}}-CH_3$$

40.

$$\overset{H_3C}{\underset{H_3C}{\diagdown}}\overset{\ominus}{\overline{C}H} \quad \overset{CH_3}{\underset{}{\overset{|}{CH}}} \overset{O}{\diagup} \quad \overset{CH_3 \quad CH_3}{CH_3-CH-CH} \quad \overset{\oplus}{MgBr}$$

$$\overset{\oplus}{MgBr} \qquad \overset{CH}{\underset{CH_3}{|}} \qquad \overset{CH-\overline{O}|^{\ominus}}{\underset{CH_3}{|}}$$

41.

$$\overset{CH_3-CH_2}{\underset{CH_3-CH_2}{\diagup}}N\overset{H}{\diagdown} \quad H-\overset{\overline{O}|}{\overset{||}{\overline{O}}}-\overset{||}{C}-CH_3 \longrightarrow \overset{CH_3-CH_2 \quad H}{\underset{CH_3-CH_2 \quad H}{N^{\oplus}}} \overset{\ominus}{\underset{}{}} \quad \overset{\overline{O}|}{|\overline{O}-\overset{||}{C}-CH_3}$$

42.

$$\overset{CH_3}{\underset{CH_3}{\overset{|}{CH_3-C-\overline{O}|^{\ominus}}}} \quad CH_3-\overline{Br}| \longrightarrow \overset{CH_3}{\underset{CH_3}{\overset{|}{CH_3-C-\overline{O}-CH_3}}} \quad |\overset{\ominus}{\overline{Br}}|$$

43. hydroxide, n, oxygen, oxygen, negative

44. hydroxide, n, pi, oxygen, oxygen, carbon, oxygen, neutral, negative,

45.

46.

47.

48. carbon, oxygen, positive, neutral

49. n, oxygen, pi, oxygen, carbon, oxygen, positive, neutral

50.

51. pi, carbon, carbon, neutral, positive,

52.

53. pi, carbon, hydrogen, neutral, positive,

54.

The alternative,

is less likely since it results in a secondary carbocation.

55. carbon, oxygen

$$CH_3-\overset{\underset{|}{|O-H}}{C}-\overset{\ominus}{\overline{O}}-CH_2-CH_3 \longrightarrow CH_3-\overset{\underset{|}{|O-H}}{\overset{\|}{C}}\overset{\overline{O}|}{}\quad \overset{\ominus}{|\overline{O}}-CH_2-CH_3$$

56.

57. carbon, oxygen, positive, neutral

58.

59. carbon, carbon, positive, neutral

60. carbon, carbon, carbon, positive, neutral

$$CH_3-CH\overset{\oplus}{\underset{\underset{H}{|}}{-}CH}-CH_3 \longrightarrow CH_3-CH=CH-CH_3\quad \overset{\oplus}{H}$$

61.

62. carbon, carbon, positive, neutral

63.

CH₃ ... CH₃ ... NO₂ ... H ... NO₂ ... H ... $\oplus$ H

64.

CH₃ ... H ... H ... $\overline{Br}$| ... CH₃ ... CH₃ ... H ... $\overline{Br}$| ... CH₃ ... $\oplus$ H

65.

CH₃ CH₃ CH₃ ... H ... C ... CH₃ ... H ... CH₃ ... H ... $\oplus$ C — CH₃ ... CH₃ ... C ... CH₃ ... H ... CH₃ ... C ... |O ... CH₃ ... |O

66.

H ... C ... $\oplus$ ... O ... H ... H

67.

H ... |O| ... $\oplus$ ... CH₃ — C ... CH₃ — C ... O| ... |O| ... O| ... H ... H ... $\oplus$ H

68.

$\overline{O}$ ... CH₂ ... CH=CH—NO₂ ... $\overline{O}$ ... |O—H ... CH₂ ... CH—$\overline{C}$H—NO₂ ... $\overline{O}$ ... |O—H

69.

$\overline{N}\equiv\overline{C}$ H C=$\ddot{O}$ CHOH   CHOH CH_2OH $\longrightarrow$ $\overline{N}\equiv C - C - \overline{O}\!\!|^{\ominus}$, H, CHOH, CHOH, CH_2OH

70.

$\overset{H}{\underset{}{N}}^{\oplus}$ (with H, H)   C $-\overline{O}-CH_3$ $\underset{}{|\underline{O}}-H$ $\longrightarrow$ H, N (H, H)   C $-\overline{O}-CH_3$ $\overset{\oplus}{O}-H$

71.

$CH_3-\overline{O}-$ (ring) $\overline{Br}|^{\oplus}$ $\longrightarrow$ $CH_3-\overline{O}-$ (ring)$^{\oplus}$ $\overline{Br}|$

72.

(phenyl)$-\overset{\prime}{O}$ $|F$ NO_2 $\ominus$ NO_2 $|\overline{F}|^{\ominus}$ $\longrightarrow$ (phenyl)$-|\underline{O}|$ NO_2 NO_2

73.

$\overset{H}{\underset{H}{|\overline{N}}}-$(cyclohexyl) $|\overline{Cl}|$ NO_2 NO_2 NO_2 $\longrightarrow$ $|\overline{Cl}|$ $\overset{\oplus}{NH_2}-$(cyclohexyl) NO_2 NO_2 $\ominus$ NO_2

74.

$\overset{\prime}{O}$, CH_2, $\overline{O}$ (ring)$-CH-CH_2-NO_2$ $|\underline{O}|^{\ominus}$ $\longrightarrow$ O, CH_2, O (ring)$-CH=\underline{\underline{O}}|$ $^{\ominus}\overline{C}H_2-NO_2$

75.

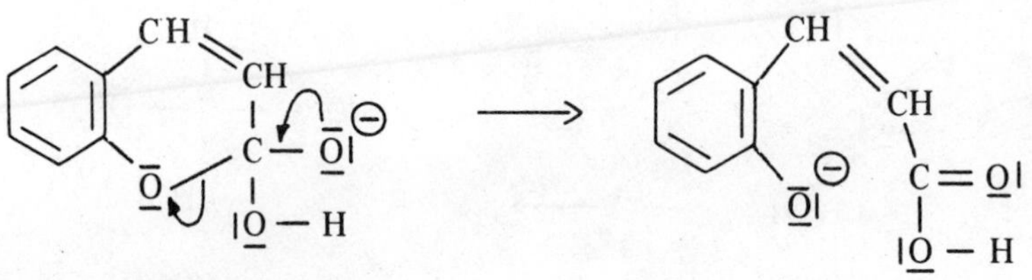

76.

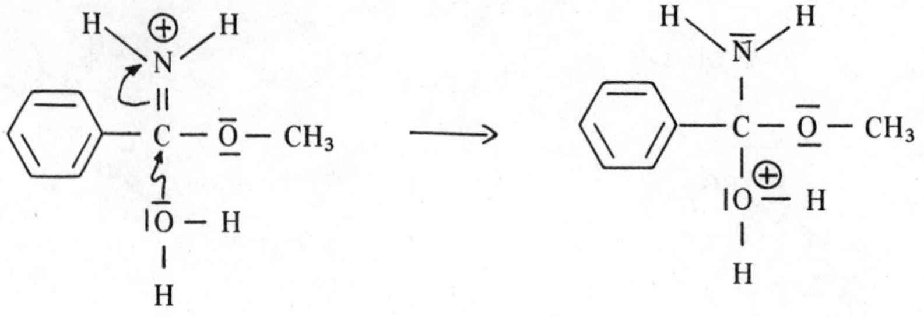

77.

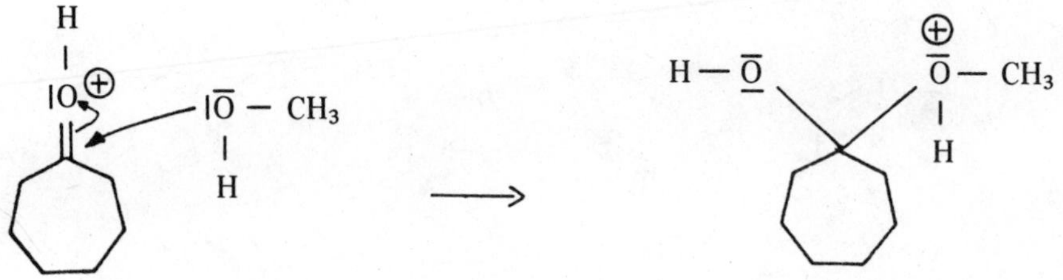

78.

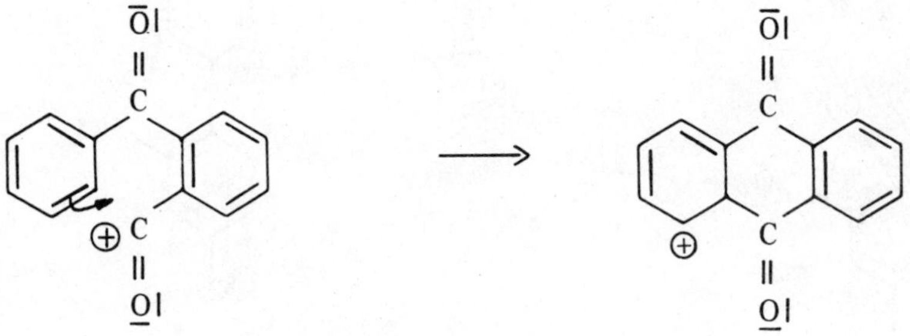

79.

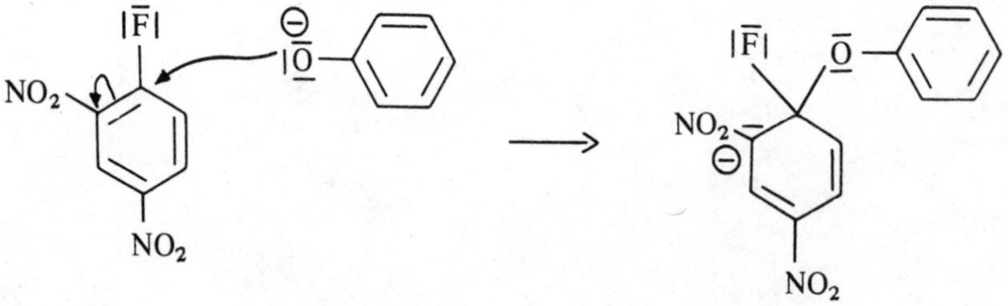

80.

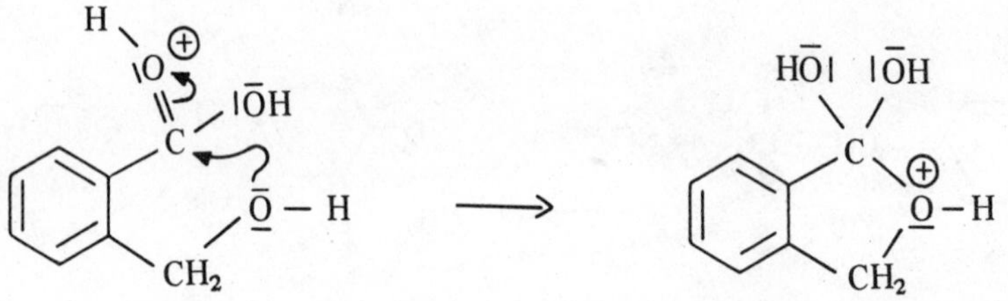

81.

82. hydrogen, carbon, neutral, negative,

83.

84. neutral, neutral,

85.

86.

87.

$$\underset{1}{CH_3} - \underset{2}{CH} = \underset{3}{CH} - \underset{4}{CH_3} \text{ , positive, negative}$$

88.

89.

90.

$$CH_3 - \underset{\underset{H}{|}}{CH} - \overset{\oplus}{CH_2}$$
$$|\underline{\overline{C}l}|^{\ominus}$$

91.

92.

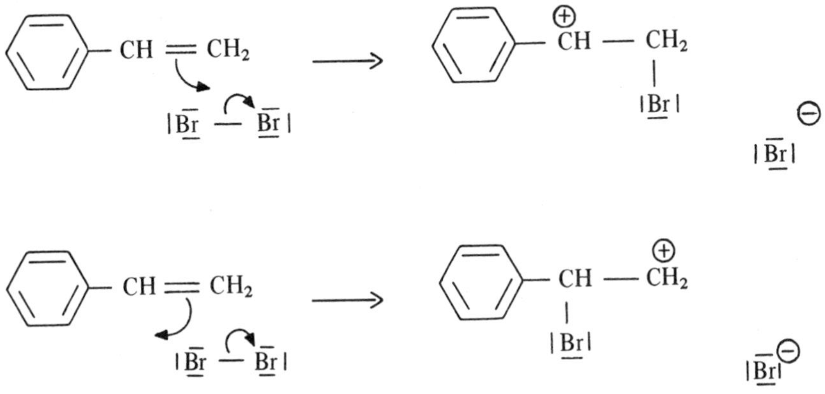

$\langle\!\!\!\!\bigcirc\!\!\!\!\rangle$—CH ＝ CH₂ $\longrightarrow$ $\langle\!\!\!\!\bigcirc\!\!\!\!\rangle$—$\overset{\oplus}{C}H$—CH₂

|B̲r — B̲r| | B̲r |

$\overset{\ominus}{|\bar{B}r|}$

$\langle\!\!\!\!\bigcirc\!\!\!\!\rangle$—CH ＝ CH₂ $\longrightarrow$ $\langle\!\!\!\!\bigcirc\!\!\!\!\rangle$—CH—$\overset{\oplus}{C}H_2$

|B̲r — B̲r| | B̲r |

$|\bar{B}r|^{\ominus}$

93.

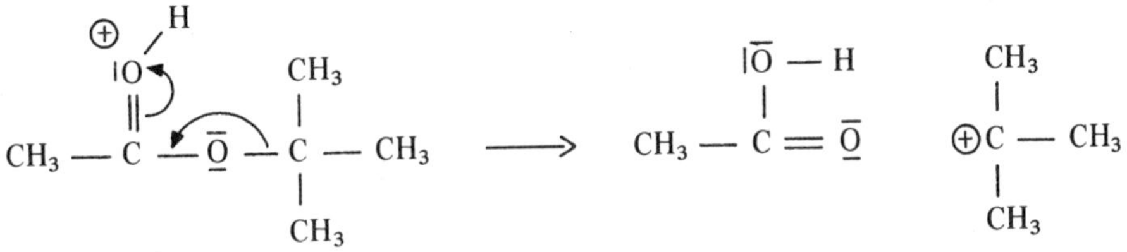

$\overset{\oplus}{\underset{||}{|O}}\!\!-\!\!H$

CH₃—C—O̲—C—CH₃ $\longrightarrow$ CH₃—C ＝ O̲ $\oplus$C—CH₃

CH₃   CH₃

|O̲—H

CH₃   CH₃

94.

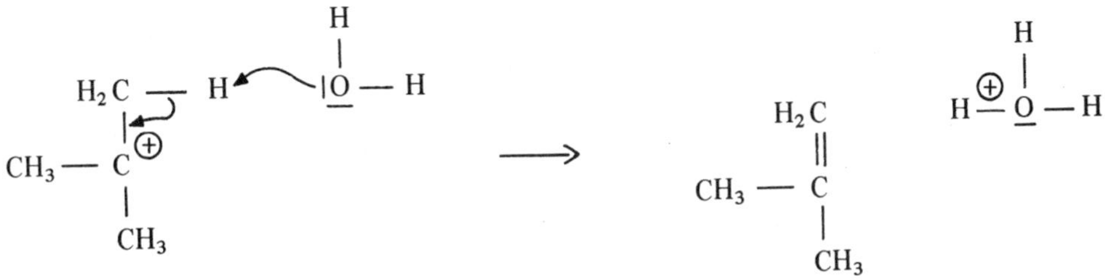

H₂C—H ← |O̲—H

  | H

CH₃—C⊕ $\longrightarrow$ H₂C

  | ‖

CH₃   CH₃—C

  | CH₃

H—$\overset{\oplus}{O̲}$—H

  | H

95.

H—O̲l

  | H

  H

  |

  |O̲|

$\langle\!\!\!\!\bigcirc\!\!\!\!\rangle$—C ＝ N̄—$\langle\!\!\!\!\bigcirc\!\!\!\!\rangle$ $\longrightarrow$

  H

  |

  |O̲$\overset{\oplus}{}$—H

  |

  H

H—O̲l$\overset{\oplus}{}$

  |

  H

$\langle\!\!\!\!\bigcirc\!\!\!\!\rangle$—C—N̄—$\langle\!\!\!\!\bigcirc\!\!\!\!\rangle$

  ‖ |

  |O| H

|O̲—H

  |

  H

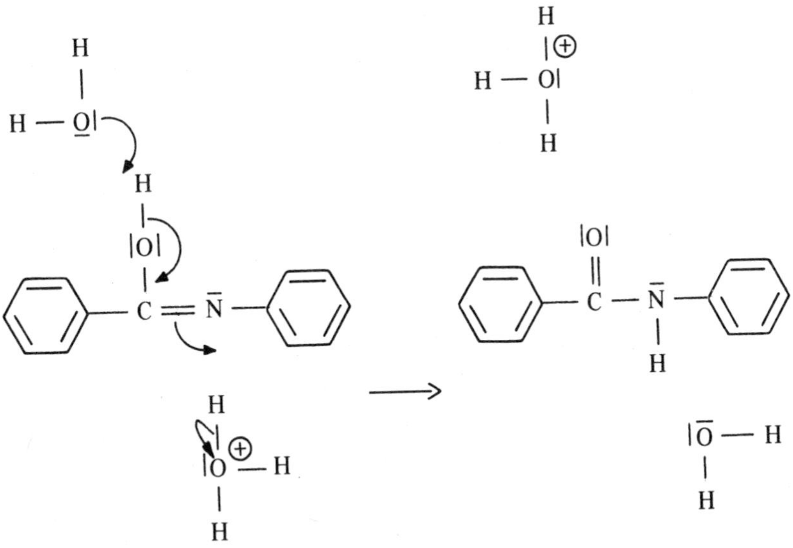

96.

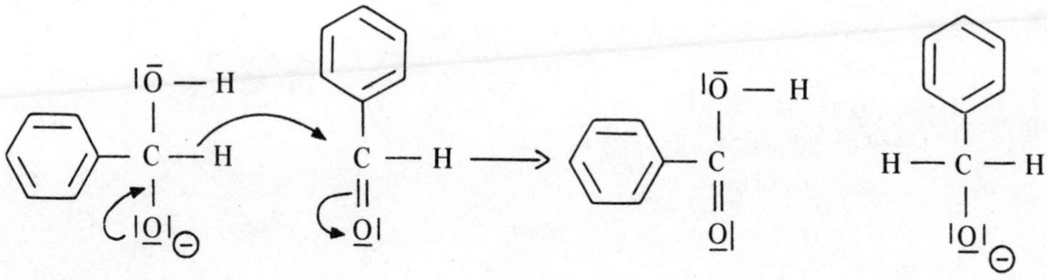

$\overline{|O} - H$

$C - H$

$|\underline{O}|^{\ominus}$

$C - H$

$\underline{O}|$

$\overline{|O} - H$

C

$\underline{O}|$

$H - C - H$

$|\underline{O}|^{\ominus}$

97.

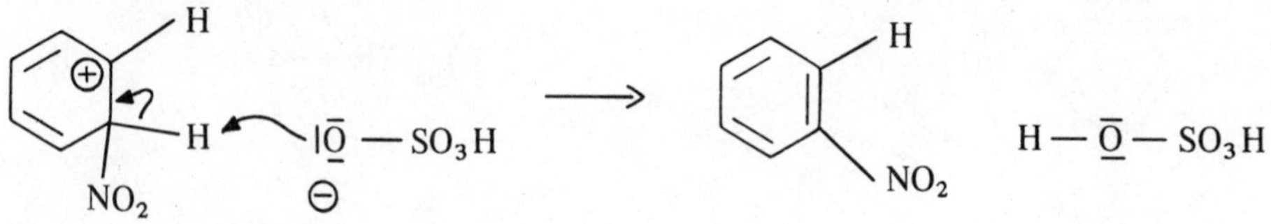

H

H

NO_2

$|\overline{O} - SO_3H$

$\ominus$

H

NO_2

$H - \overline{\underline{O}} - SO_3H$

98.

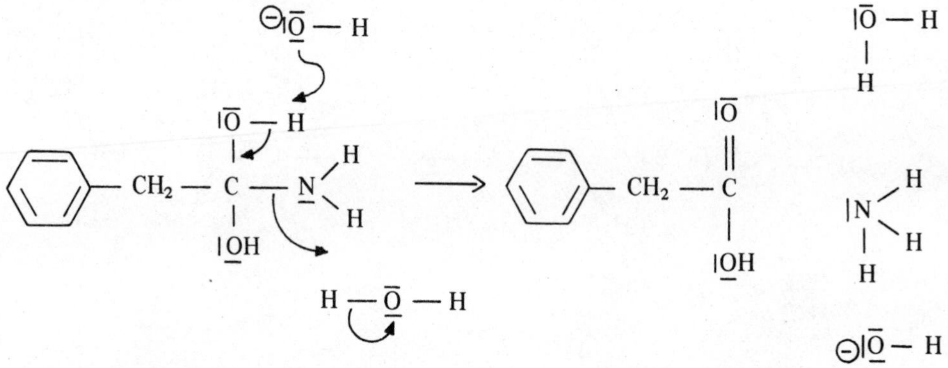

$\ominus|\overline{\underline{O}} - H$

$|\overline{O} - H$

$CH_2 - C - N$

$|\underline{OH}$

H

H

$H - \overline{\underline{O}} - H$

$CH_2 - C$

$|\overline{O}$

$\underline{O}$

$|\underline{OH}$

$|\overline{O} - H$

H

$|N$

H

H

H

$\ominus|\overline{\underline{O}} - H$

99.

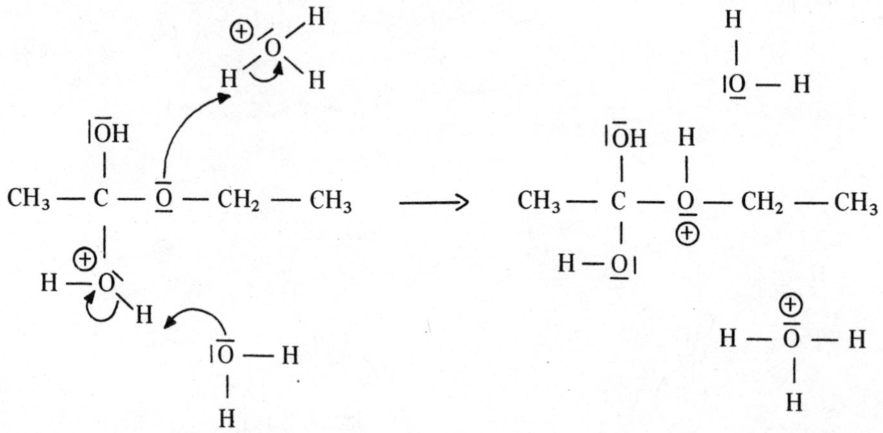

$\oplus O$

H

H

H

$|\overline{OH}$

$CH_3 - C - \underline{\overline{O}} - CH_2 - CH_3$

$\oplus$

$H - O$

H

$|\overline{O} - H$

H

H

$|\underline{O} - H$

$|\overline{OH}$

H

$CH_3 - C - O - CH_2 - CH_3$

$\oplus$

$H - \underline{O}|$

$\oplus$

$H - \overline{O} - H$

H

100.

CH_3

$CH_3 - C - CH_2$

$\oplus$

H

CH_3

$CH_3 - C - CH_2$

$\oplus$

H

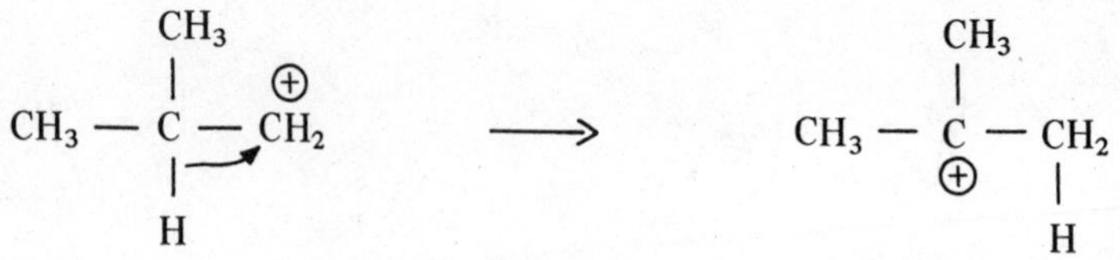

101.

$$CH_3 - \overset{\overset{\displaystyle CH_3}{|}}{\underset{\oplus}{C}} - \overset{\underset{\displaystyle CH_3}{|}}{CH} - CH_3$$

102.

103.

104.

105.

106.

107.

108.

109.

110.

111.

112.

113.

114.

115.

116.

117.

118.

119.

120.

121.

122.

123.

124.

125.

GLOSSARY OF TERMS

Aliphatic. One of two broad classes of organic compounds. The other is "aromatic." Aliphatic compounds are composed of chains of carbon atoms. A subgroup within this class is the alicyclic compounds which contain rings of carbon atoms but are similar to open-chain compounds in chemical and physical properties. Actually, the most sensible definition of aliphatic compounds is "compounds that are not aromatic."

Aromatic. One of two broad classes of organic compounds. The other is "aliphatic." Benzene, compounds containing a benzene ring, and compounds similar to benzene in chemical properties constitute the aromatic compounds.

Carbanion. An ion in which a negative charge resides on a carbon atom.

Carbocation. An ion in which a positive charge resides on a carbon atom. Most organic text books use the term "carbonium ion" for the kind of carbocation found in this text. However, the term "carbenium ion" has been proposed as a more systematic name. Carbenium ion appears in the research literature and in some texts. This author has chosen to hedge his bets by using the more general term, carbocation.

Double Bond. The combination of a sigma bond and a pi bond between two atoms. The carbon-carbon double bond is written $\diagdown C = C \diagdown$
In this notation there is no convention regarding which line represents the sigma, and which, the pi bond. The presence of a double bond makes a compound unsaturated.

Electron Attracting and Electron Releasing Groups. Various groups of atoms which are found in organic compounds are electron attracting or releasing, relative to the carbon atom to which they are attached. The presence of these groups can have a marked effect on chemical reactivity. Some electron releasing groups are: $-NH_2$, $-OCH_3$, $-CH_3$, etc. Some electron attracting groups are: $-NO_2$, $-COOH$, $-F$, $-Cl$, $-Br$, $-CN$, etc.

Electrophile. The word comes from the Greek meaning "electron lover." Electrophiles are chemical entities (atoms, ions, radicals, or molecules) which seek electrons. Electrophiles are electron-poor. They are designated as E or $E^\oplus$. When an electrophile reacts with some electron-rich center on an organic molecule the process is called electrophilic attack.

Formal Charge. A Lewis structure is, after all, only a graphic representation of a molecular structure. As useful as they are, Lewis structures are not entirely descriptive of a molecule. The formal charge is the charge which would be on an atom in a molecule if the Lewis structure were an entirely accurate representation of the molecule. In one sense, formal charge is simply electron bookkeeping. However, the location of formal charge on a Lewis structure is always revealing as to the chemistry of the molecule.

Functional Group. One can think of organic compounds as being composed of two parts: a hydrocarbon backbone and a functional group. The latter is an atom or group of atoms which confer some distinct chemical or physical property. The functional group is the site of chemical reactions. Thus, molecules with the same functional group undergo similar chemical reactions despite having quite different hydrocarbon backbones.

Grignard Reagent. A reagent formed by reaction of an alkyl halide with magnesium in an ether solvent. These reagents are extremely useful and versatile intermediates for synthesizing organic compounds. The actual structure of the Grignard reagent is rather complex. It is expedient, however, to consider it an ion pair, as this text does.

Heterolytic Cleavage (Heterolysis). The breaking of a bond so that the electrons which formed the bond are distributed unevenly between the two fragments. Heterolysis results in an anion and a cation.

$$A - B \longrightarrow A^\oplus + B^\ominus$$

$$\text{or} \quad A - B \longrightarrow A^\ominus + B^\oplus$$

The counterpart of heterolysis is homolysis in which the electrons are distributed evenly between the two fragments. The result is a pair of radicals.

$$A \text{---} B \longrightarrow A\cdot \quad + \quad B\cdot$$

Non-bonding (n) Electrons. Valence electrons in a molecule which are not involved in binding one atom to another. In a Lewis structure they are the exclusive property of one atom. They are also called "unshared" electrons.

Nucleophile. The word comes from the Greek, meaning "nucleus lover." Nucleophiles are chemical entities (ions or molecules) which seek an electron-poor center. Nucleophiles are electron-rich. They are designated as Nu or $Nu^{\ominus}$. When a nucleophile reacts with some electron-poor center of an organic molecule, the process is called nucleophilic attack.

Pi Bond and Pi Electrons. Bonds that are the result of lateral (side to side) overlap of atomic p-orbitals. Pi bonds are weaker than sigma bonds. Pi bonds are always found in combination with a sigma bond. Therefore, single bonds are never pi bonds. Pi electrons are the electrons in pi bonds.

Primary Carbocation. Carbocations are classified as primary, secondary, or tertiary according to the following scheme.

Primary: The carbon atom having the positive charge is <u>directly</u> attached to only one other carbon atom and two hydrogen atoms. For example:

$$\overset{\displaystyle H}{\underset{\displaystyle H}{\overset{|}{\underset{|}{\oplus C}}}} - CH_3$$

Secondary: The carbon atom having the positive charge is directly attached to two other carbon atoms and one hydrogen atom. For example:

$$\overset{\displaystyle CH_3}{\underset{\displaystyle H}{\overset{|}{\underset{|}{\oplus C}}}} - CH_3$$

Tertiary: The carbon atom having the positive charge is directly attached to three other carbon atoms and no hydrogen atoms. For example:

$$\underset{\underset{CH_3}{|}}{\overset{\overset{CH_3}{|}}{\oplus\;C-CH_3}}$$

The order of stability of carbocations is:
tertiary > secondary > primary

Protonation. The combination of a proton (hydrogen ion) with some organic base to give the conjugate acid of that base.

$$H^{\oplus} \quad + \quad \bar{B} \longrightarrow [H - B]^{\oplus}$$

Saturated. Compounds which contain only single bonds cannot add other reagents. Thus, they are called "saturated."

Secondary Carbocation. (See primary carbocation.)

Sigma Bond and Sigma Electrons. Bonds that are the result of axial overlap of atomic orbitals. All single bonds are sigma bonds. Sigma electrons are the electrons in sigma bonds.

S_N1 and S_N2. Organic reactions can be classified according to their mechanisms. The S_N1 and S_N2 reactions are probably the best known of these. This classification gives: the result, the type of reagent, and the molecularity of the reaction. Thus, S_N1 stands for "substitution, nucleophilic, unimolecular," and S_N2 stands for "substitution, nucleophilic, bimolecular."

Solvolysis. A reaction in which a molecule of the solvent is one of the reactants.

Stereochemistry. The study of the arrangement of atoms in three-dimensional space, and how the arrangement affects the chemical and physical properties of molecules.

Steric Strain. Strain (instability) present in a molecule because of the arrangement of the atoms. Steric strain usually arises because bond angles are forced to depart from their ideal value, or because non-bonded atoms are required to be too close to one another.

Tertiary Carbocation. (See primary carbocation.)

Unsaturated. Compounds which contain double or triple bonds are capable of adding other reagents. Thus, they are called "unsaturated."

Unshared Electron Pairs. (See non-bonding electrons.)